THE
USBORNE
FIRST BOOK
OF
KNOWLEDGE

VOLUME 2

WILD ANIMALS
CATS AND KITTENS
DOGS AND PUPPIES
SMALL PETS
BIRDS

CREEPY CRAWLIES
BUTTERFLIES AND MOTHS
FISHES
TREES
FLOWERS

Barbara Cork, Rosamund Kidman Cox, Alwyne Wheeler, Ruth Thomson, Rose Hill, Cathy Kilpatrick

Designed by
David Bennett, Anne Sharples, Andrzej Bielecki, Clare Clements

Illustrated by
Denise Finney, David Wright, Dee Morgan, Judy Friedlander, Joyce Bee, David Hurrell, Richard Lewington, Mick Loates, Andy Martin, Liz Pepperell, Chris Shields, Roy Hutchison, Elaine Keenan, Robert Morton, John Sibbick, John Thompson-Steinkrauss, Malcolm McGregor, Coral Sealey, Martin Camm, Andrzej Bielecki, Bob Bampton, Wendy Bramall, Paul Brooks, Frankie Coventry, Sarah Fox-Davies, Dee McLean, David More, Ralph Stobart, Sally Voke, James Woods, Mark Burgess, Michelle Emblem, Victoria Gooman, Cynthia Pow, David Nockels, Frederick St Ward, Ian Jackson, David Hall, Paul Crompton, Anne Sharples

This edition first published in 1995 by
Usborne Publishing Ltd, 83-85 Saffron Hill,
London EC1N 8RT, England.

Copyright © 1995, 1991, 1982, 1980,
Usborne Publishing Ltd.

Printed in Italy.

CONTENTS

WILD ANIMALS

A Wood Mouse is hidden
near this Leopard. Can
you find 15 more Wood
Mice hidden in the Wild
Animals pages?

Looking at mammals

Mammals are different from all the other animals in the world. They are the only animals that have fur or hair. Female mammals are the only animals that produce milk to feed to their young. You are a mammal.

Fallow Deer feeding her fawn.

All mammals breathe air, even mammals that live in water.

A mammal has a good brain.

All mammals have some fur or hair on their body.

Musk Oxen have lots of hair. This keeps them warm.

Porcupines have special hairs, called quills.

Elephants ▶ have only a few hairs.

Many mammals have two kinds of hair in their coat. Beavers have a thick layer of short, soft hairs under a layer of long, rough hairs. Only the long hairs get wet in water.

Bactrian Camel

Some mammals, such as Camels, grow two new coats every year. This Camel is growing its thin summer coat. Its thick winter coat falls out so fast that the hairs come off in large chunks.

winter coat

summer coat

3

Legs and feet

Most mammals move around on four legs.

ankle

Pandas walk on their whole foot.

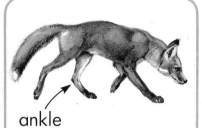

ankle

Foxes walk on their toes.

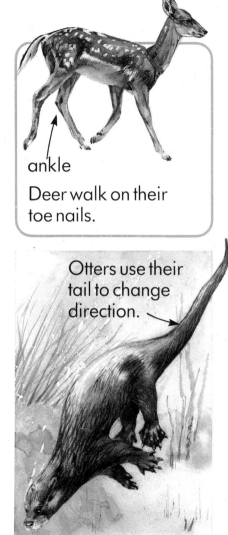

ankle

Deer walk on their toe nails.

Otters use their tail to change direction.

Back feet land in front of front feet.

Mountain Hares have feet like snowshoes. Their feet are wide and flat and have lots of fur underneath. This helps them to walk or run over the snow without sinking in very far.

Otters have skin between their toes. They use their feet like flippers to push them through the water.

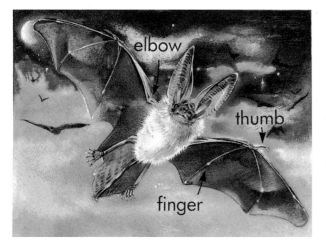

elbow

thumb

finger

The only mammals that can fly are bats. They use their arms as wings. Each wing is made of skin. The skin is stretched over the bones of the arms and fingers.

Long, thin toes for holding on to branches.

Kangaroo Rats hop around on two legs. They use their long back legs to make huge leaps. Their tail helps them to balance.

Spider Monkeys use their strong tail like an extra arm or leg. They curl the tip of the tail around branches to help them swing through the trees.

Teeth and feeding

Many mammals feed mainly on plants. They have a lot of grinding teeth because plants are hard to chew.

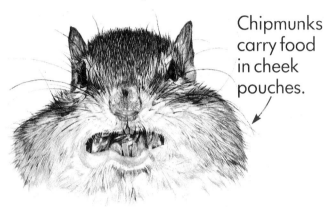

Chipmunks carry food in cheek pouches.

Horny pad is under here.

The front teeth of a Chipmunk never stop growing. Its teeth do not get too long as it wears them down when it feeds.

Bighorn Sheep have no front teeth in their top jaw. Instead they have a horny pad to bite off the tops of plants.

Long tongue pulls leaves off branches.

Zebra

Dik-dik

Eland

Giraffe

Many different mammals can feed close together on the African grasslands. This is because they eat different kinds of plants and feed at different heights. You can see this if you look carefully at the mammals in the picture above.

fruit

Dead Vole

Long, sensitive fingers help to find and catch food.

fish

Koalas feed only on the leaves of Gum Trees. They will die if they cannot find the right sort of Gum Tree to feed on.

Racoons feed on plants and animals. They eat living things and dead things. They can usually find enough to eat.

Long, pointed teeth to grip an animal's throat and strangle it.

Cheetah

Gazelle

Razor-sharp cheek teeth to tear meat.

Some mammals feed mainly on other animals. They use up a lot of energy catching their food. Cheetahs may be too tired to eat for up to 15 minutes after they have killed an animal. But meat is very nourishing, so they do not feed every day.

Mammals at night

More than half the mammals in the world come out at night.

Pupil opens wide to let in lots of light.

Sticky pads on toes help to grip branches.

Potto

Many mammals have a special layer at the back of their eyes. This layer helps them to see in the dark. It makes their eyes glow if a light shines on them.

The Tarsier has huge eyes and special ears that help it to see and hear well at night. It leaps through the trees and pounces on insects and small animals.

Badgers use their sharp sense of smell and good hearing to move around and feed at night. They find food by sniffing the ground with their sensitive noses.

fold of skin

Many bats feed on the insects that come out at night. This Greater Horseshoe Bat eats flies, beetles and moths. It has sharp pointed teeth to chop up its food.

Sugar Gliders feed on flowers and insects at night. They stretch open the folds of skin along the sides of their bodies to glide quietly from tree to tree.

The Red Fox hunts at night. When it hears and smells a mouse in the grass, the Fox leaps up in the air like this. It will land with its front paws on the mouse.

Escaping from enemies

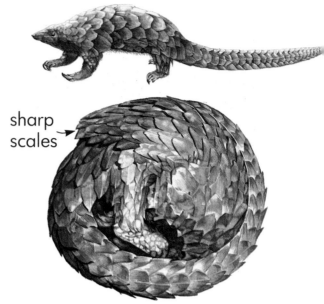

sharp scales

Squirrels escape from enemies by climbing trees. They are small and light and can leap on to very thin branches. Most of their enemies cannot follow.

Pangolins have horny scales like a suit of armour. The back edge of each scale is sharp. When they roll into a tight ball, their enemies cannot hurt them.

1. This Spiny Anteater has sharp spines on its back. It burrows into the ground to escape enemies.

2. It digs straight down with its long claws and sinks out of sight in about one minute.

3. When it is buried, its enemies leave it alone. The spines may cut them if they try to dig it up.

Skunk holds tail up to say "Go away or I will squirt you with smelly liquid".

summer

winter

Skunks squirt a nasty liquid at enemies. The liquid comes from a gland under the tail. Most enemies leave them alone.

The Mountain Hare lives in places where it snows in winter. It has a white coat in winter and a brown coat in summer. This helps it to hide from enemies, such as Foxes.

Many mammals that live in forests or jungles have stripes or spots on their fur. They match the colours and patterns on the trees and bushes. This helps them to hide from their enemies. There are eight mammals in this African jungle. Can you find them all?

Homes

Mammals build homes to keep them warm, dry and safe from enemies.

Rabbits live in a maze of tunnels, which they dig under the ground. Their home is called a warren. They run into the warren to escape from enemies.

The female Harvest Mouse builds a home for her young. She tears grass leaves into strips and weaves them into a round nest. It is warm and dry inside.

The cubs are born in the middle of winter.

The female Polar Bear digs a cave of ice and snow to spend the winter in. She does not come out until the weather gets warmer in spring.

The only home Chimpanzees make is a nest to sleep in. They build the nest near the top of a tree. They bend branches over to make a cushion of leaves.

A Mole spends most of its life inside its home. It uses its front feet like shovels to dig out tunnels in the soil. It feeds and sleeps in these tunnels.

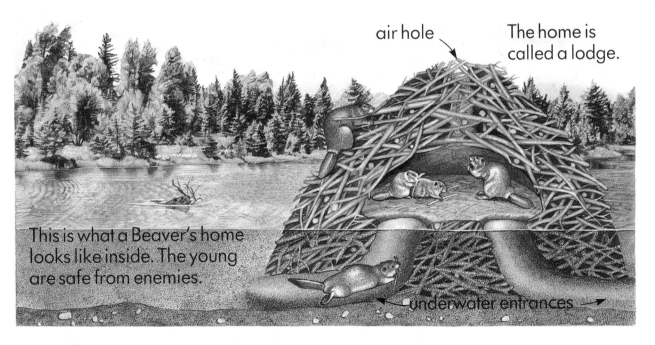

air hole

The home is called a lodge.

This is what a Beaver's home looks like inside. The young are safe from enemies.

underwater entrances

13

Finding a mate

female

male

Siberian Tiger

male

Female mammals often give off a special smell when they are ready to mate. A male Harvest Mouse sniffs a female to see if she is ready to mate.

Tigers play together before they mate. This female is asking the male to mate with her. She bites him gently and then rubs her body against his.

females

The antlers fall off when the mating season ends.

Once a year, a male Red Deer rounds up a group of females for mating. He roars loudly to tell other males how strong he is. If another male roars as often as he does, they fight with their antlers. The strongest male wins the females.

Male antelopes, such as this Uganda Kob, have to dance in front of a female before they mate with her.

male female male female

1. The male Kob holds his head up to show off the white patch under his chin. He stretches out his front legs to show off his black stripes.

2. Then he holds his front leg out very stiff and straight. He taps the female's side gently. If she stands still, he will mate with her.

Male and female Red Foxes dance together before they mate. They stand on their back legs and hug each other with their front legs. They hold their mouths open and make a chattering call.

15

Eggs and birth

After a female mammal has mated, a baby may start to grow inside her. Most baby mammals stay inside their mother until they have grown all the parts of their bodies. Then they are ready to be born.

When Zebras are born, they can see, hear and smell and have hair all over their bodies. They can run about an hour after they are born. They stay close to the other Zebras. This helps to keep them safe from enemies.

birth sac

When Dormice are born, they are helpless. They are blind and deaf and have no hair on their bodies. They are born in a nest, which helps to keep them warm and safe from enemies.

A few mammals are born before they grow all the parts of their bodies. Most of them finish developing in a pouch on their mother's body.

pouch

Close-up of the birth opening. The baby climbs upwards.

As soon as a baby Kangaroo is born, it has to crawl from the birth opening up to its mother's pouch. This takes about three minutes. The baby is so small, it would fit into a teaspoon.

Looking inside the pouch

The baby holds on to a teat and sucks milk from its mother. It stays in the pouch for six months. By then, it has grown all the parts of its body.

The Platypus and the Spiny Anteaters are unusual mammals that lay eggs. A baby grows inside each egg.

The Platypus lays her eggs in a nest of leaves and grass. The eggs have a soft shell.

The nest is at the end of a long burrow in a river bank.

Growing up

Japanese Macaque

The baby stays with its mother for two or three years.

White-tailed Deer

Most mammals spend a lot of time licking their young. This keeps them clean and healthy. It also forms a bond between mother and young.

A baby mammal sucks milk from glands on its mother's body. The glands produce milk as soon as a baby is born. The milk is rich in foods the baby needs.

A Tigress picks up her cubs in her mouth to carry them to a safe place. The cubs do not get hurt as they keep still and their mother's jaws do not shut properly.

African Elephant

Mountain Goats play games with their mother and the other young goats. This helps them to learn how to balance and climb on the steep mountain slopes.

This mother Elephant is protecting her calf from an enemy. The young Elephant is too small to look after itself. It stays close to its mother.

White-toothed Shrews go out with their mother when they are about a week old. They hold on to each other in a long line so they do not get lost.

19

Living in a group

Lions live in a group called a pride. The female Lions are called Lionesses. They do most of the hunting. They also feed the cubs and look after them. The male Lions keep a safe area for the pride to live in.

Lionesses hunt in teams. They are more likely to catch large animals if they hunt together.

An adult male has a thick mane. This protects his head and neck in fights. It also helps him to attract a female.

This is a young male. He will leave the pride when he is about three years old.

The cubs spend a lot of time playing. This helps them learn how to fight and hunt.

A Lioness usually stays in the pride for life. She may feed any of the cubs. This helps them survive.

Chimpanzees live in a group called a community. The males defend the group from enemies. They often travel and feed with other males. Females look after the young.

A Chimpanzee may share its food with other Chimps in the group. One Chimp may stare at another to ask for food.

There is a top male in each group. He often charges about like this making a lot of noise. This shows the other Chimps he is in charge.

Chimps crouch down like this when they meet a more important Chimp. This Chimp may pat them to say "I will not attack you".

Woodland Chimps catch Termites by poking a grass stem into their nest. Young Chimps watch their parents to find out how to do this.

Chimpanzees spend a lot of time grooming their fur. This helps to keep them clean and healthy. Grooming also calms the Chimps and helps them to stay good friends.

Sea Mammals

The only mammals that spend their whole lives in the sea are Dolphins, Whales and Sea Cows. They have few hairs and no back legs.

A Dolphin comes to the surface to breathe air through its blowhole.

A Dolphin's teeth are all the same. They are good for catching fish.

A Dolphin's body is a good shape for moving fast through the water. It moves its strong tail up and down to push it along. It uses its flippers and the fin on its back to change direction.

Mouth of a Humpback Whale.

bony plates

Some Whales have no teeth. Instead they have rows of bony plates, which end in a thick, hairy fringe. The fringe strains tiny animals from the sea water.

Manatees are a kind of Sea Cow.

This Manatee calf is sucking milk from a teat near its mother's flipper. Manatees are born in the water and can swim as soon as they are born.

Seals, Sea Lions and Walruses spend only part of their lives in the sea. They have back legs and most of them have a coat of short hair.

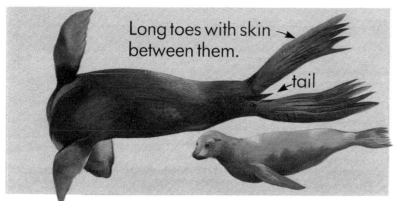

Long toes with skin between them.

tail

A Sea Lion's smooth, thin body helps it to swim fast underwater. It uses its front flippers to push it along. It uses its back flippers to change direction. It has only a short tail.

Walruses use their long teeth to dig up shellfish from the sea floor. They also use their teeth for fighting.

Pups grow fast on their mother's rich milk.

A layer of skin comes off with the old fur coat.

Seals, Sea Lions and Walruses come out of the sea every year to give birth, mate and grow a new coat of fur.
This is a group of Elephant Seals. The males fight each other to win their own area on the beach. They will mate with all the females in their area.

Picture puzzle

The Rabbit has to get back to his home on the other side of the maze. Can you help him to find the right path? Part of the maze goes through the Giraffe's body. Can you name all the mammals in the maze?

START

HOME

CATS AND KITTENS

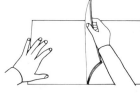

Watch the cat run

Hold the Cat pages like this.

Watch the top right hand corner and flick the pages over fast.

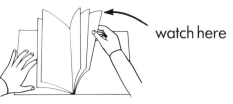

watch here

Being a cat owner

Before you get a cat, there are some important things to think about. First, make sure that everyone at home agrees to have a pet.

A cat can live for 15 years. You will have to look after it every day. Never abandon a cat – in some countries it's against the law.

If you go away for more than a day, you will have to make sure someone else can feed and look after the cat.

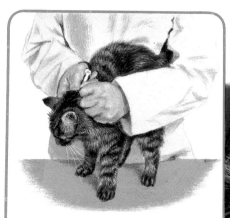

Keeping a cat can be expensive. Food, vet's bills, and stays in a cattery all cost money.

Your cat will need your company. It will enjoy being stroked by you. Cats purr when they are happy. They are friendly if they are looked after properly.

(But sometimes your cat will want to be alone.)

Cats are exciting to watch. They move beautifully. They don't need to be taken for a walk, but they do like to go out by themselves. It's unfair to get a cat if you live on a busy road or by a railway. Why do you think this is?

Cats are related to wild cats like lions and tigers. They like to hunt outside.

If you have another pet

You should always keep any fishes or small pet animals away from your cat's reach. Small animals may die of fright.

Don't leave a cat and dog together until they have got used to each other. Then they may become friends.

Getting a cat

It's best to choose your kitten when it is still with its mother. You can find your kitten through advertisements, friends, the vet or a local animal welfare society. Never take a cat from the street. It may have a good home somewhere.

Long-haired cats need a lot of grooming.

Pedigree cats are bred for their looks. They are expensive to buy and may need a lot of care and attention.

You can take a kitten home when it is 8 weeks old. Kittens grow quickly. When they are very young, you can tell their age by what they do:

1. When kittens are only a few hours old they can't see or walk.

2. After 8-10 days, their eyes are open and they can walk.

3. At 4 weeks they can climb out of the "nest".

4. By the time they are 5-6 weeks old, they become daring and play with anything.

5. After 8 weeks, they no longer need their mother's milk. They eat solid food.

How to choose a kitten

When you choose from a family of kittens, watch them all for as long as possible. Try to pick the kitten with the brightest eyes that is also clean, curious and playful. It must be able to run properly. Check that the mother is healthy as well.

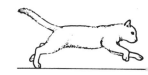

All kittens are different. Some are strong and active.

Some are timid and take longer to learn.

Others are curious and may get into trouble.

Your kitten's new home

Before you bring your kitten home, there are seven things you should have ready. They are shown on these two pages.

1. You will need a basket or box to carry your kitten home in. A strong cardboard box will do but it must be tightly shut.

The box must have lots of air holes.

The kitten should be able to turn around inside.

2. You will need three bowls for food, water and milk.

4. You could buy or make a few toys for your kitten to play with.

cooking foil

bell

Empty spool on a piece of string.

ping-pong balls

3. Your kitten will need a litter tray indoors because it will not be able to go outside at first. Don't put the tray next to its bed or its food.

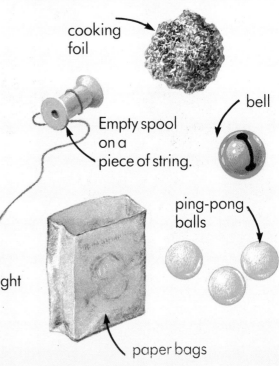

newspaper

Fill the tray with sand, earth or a cat litter bought from a supermarket or a pet store.

paper bags

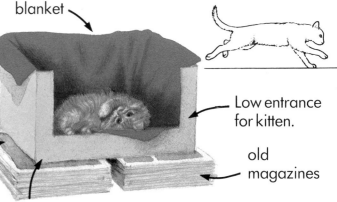

5. You will need a brush and a metal comb. If you groom your kitten when it is young, it will soon get used to being brushed.

blanket

Low entrance for kitten.

old magazines

Raise the bed a little way off the ground to keep the kitten warm and out of draughts.

6. Give your kitten a bed in a warm, quiet place. You could use a basket or a cardboard box with a blanket inside.

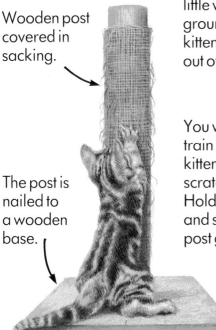

Wooden post covered in sacking.

The post is nailed to a wooden base.

You will have to train a young kitten to use a scratching post. Hold its paw and scratch the post gently.

7. Cats need to sharpen their claws. If there is nothing else, your kitten may scratch the furniture. Give it a piece of soft wood instead, or get someone to help you make a scratching post like this one. You can also buy special boards to hang on the wall.

Your kitten may be timid at first. But after a few days, it will become bolder and more curious. When it has settled down, take it to the vet for a check up. Ask about infections against diseases and about neutering (see page 46).

Feeding cats and kittens

Cats and kittens are fussy eaters. You can feed them on fresh foods, or on good quality tinned cat and kitten foods, or on a mixture of both.

When your kitten begins to eat solid food, give it 4 small meals a day. When it is 4 months old, start cutting down the number of meals to 3 larger ones a day. When it is about 8 months old, it should need only 2 larger meals a day.

Kittens need good food to grow strong and healthy. The easiest way to feed a kitten is to give it good quality tinned kitten food. You can also feed it on fresh foods (meat, fish, breakfast cereal, brown bread and milk). Ask your vet about vitamins and minerals and for advice about a balanced diet for your kitten. Never give a cat tinned dog food.

Give your kitten **milk** every mealtime until it is 4 months old. Older kittens should have milk only once or twice a day. Fully grown cats don't really need milk but they may like a little sometimes. Some cats don't like milk. **All cats and kittens need water.** Always leave fresh water out for your pet so that it can drink whenever it wants to.

Cats and kittens like to be fed at the same time every day, in the same quiet corner. A short while after the cat has finished eating, take the bowl away and wash it.

Chicken bones

Even well-fed cats will steal food.

Don't let your cat have any small, sharp bones like chicken bones. They might make the cat choke. Wrap the bones up and put them in a bin with a tight-fitting lid.

Teeth

Cats are mainly meat-eaters. They have long, sharp canine teeth for tearing meat. Their cheek teeth are used to cut the meat up into small pieces. A kitten can't cut up its own food.

Canine tooth

cheek teeth

Dry food is good for your cat's teeth, but you must leave water nearby as well.

33

Sleeping

Cats sleep about 15 hours a day. You can give your cat its own bed, but it will sleep wherever it wants to.

They like to sleep in warm places.

They like tight places to squeeze themselves into.

Sometimes they pick odd places.

They like to sleep in hidden places. Before you close a door, make sure the cat isn't inside.

Cats often sleep lightly. Their ears can pick up sounds and they can wake up quickly.

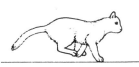

Sometimes cats sleep soundly. They will sleep like this only when they feel safe. They often curl right round in a ball. If the cat dreams, it may twitch and make little noises.

When cats wake up, they stretch their bodies.

They may yawn first.

They stretch their front legs.

They stretch their back legs.

Then they arch their back right up like this.

Don't put your cat out at night. It might get cold or wet or be hurt in a road accident.

Playing

Cats and kittens love to play and explore.

They will play with you...

Be careful if the cat sees your fingers moving. It might go for them instead of the toy.

...or by themselves.

Don't let your cat play with small things like marbles, which it could swallow, or sharp things, like scissors or needles.

Kittens learn to hunt when they play. They learn to hide in wait, listen for their prey and then track it down. They practise killing animals by jumping on toys.

1. First they watch the prey. They will sometimes do this for a long time.

2. Then they slowly stalk the prey. They move without making a sound.

3. Suddenly they pounce on the prey and bite it to kill it. Often they play with the prey afterwards.

Playing with your cat

Cats like toys that make a noise, such as crumpled up newspaper. Don't frighten the cat with a loud or sudden noise.

Don't leave wool or string lying around. Your cat may swallow some or get its claws caught.

If you leave an empty box or a paper bag on the floor, your cat may like to dive inside it to explore. Don't let the cat play with plastic bags. It could suffocate.

Cats love climbing. They have a good sense of balance. Their tail helps them to balance.

Let the cat catch the toy from time to time otherwise it will get bored.

Strong claws to grip branch.

37

Training

Cats will do what they like. They cannot be trained like dogs. But there are some things that they can learn, such as using a litter tray or a cat flap or coming when you call their name.

Show your kitten where its new tray is. Put it in the tray after meals and in the morning and at night.

Kittens are trained by their mother to use a litter tray.

Cats are very clean animals. When they go to the lavatory, they use a hole that they have dug. Then they cover it up. Clean out the litter tray every week and change the litter every day. Then wash your hands. If you want to train your cat to use a garden, move the litter tray gradually nearer the door. After a few days, put the tray outside the door.

Cat flap fixed in a door.

When your kitten is about 4 months old, train it to use a cat flap. Put the kitten just outside before it has its meal. Let it see its food through the open flap. When it comes through the flap, give it the food. Do this before each meal until it learns to use the flap.

It is easier to stop your cat from learning bad habits than it is to teach it new ones. If you find the cat doing something you don't want it to do, say "no" firmly and move the cat away.
Never hit your cat.

elastic

Hunting is in a cat's nature. But you can make it difficult for the cat to catch birds if you put a bell on a collar.

Cats often scratch the furniture unless you give them a piece of soft wood or a scratching post to use (see page 31).

Cats may steal food even when they aren't hungry! They are acrobats, so make sure any food is well out of their reach.

If you don't want your cat to sleep on the beds, keep the bedroom doors closed.

Handling your cat

Your kitten may miss its mother at first. It will enjoy the comfort of being held and stroked. Always handle a cat or kitten gently.

Use both your hands to hold your cat or kitten. Put one hand under the front paws and use the other hand to support the cat's bottom.

Talk to your kitten and use its name. Stroke it gently in the same direction that the fur grows.

Your kitten may let you know when it wants to be stroked, to play or to sleep. Don't bother it too much or it will get overtired and angry.

Your cat will come to you when it wants your company. When it rubs against your legs like this, it is saying "I feel friendly".

When you play with your kitten, don't leave it in a high place. It may hurt itself when it tries to get down. Never drop it from a height either.

Grooming

Cats need grooming. Brush your kitten for short periods each day so that it gets used to being groomed.

If you have a long-haired cat, brush and comb it every day. Remove things caught in the fur before they make a tangle. Don't pull knots — be patient and tease them out slowly. Short-haired cats need brushing when they are moulting.

Brush the cat all over in the direction that the fur grows.

Washing

Cats spend a lot of time cleaning themselves. They don't need baths and hate water. Their rough tongue acts like a comb. They use their front paw like a sponge to wash their face.

Cats can reach almost any part of their body, because they are so flexible.

Kittens soon start to wash themselves like their mother.

41

Leaving home

Travelling

Most cats hate travelling and will try to escape. It is a good idea to get a cat used to travelling while it is still a kitten. You will need a strong box or basket to carry your cat in.

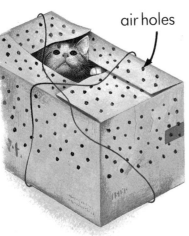

air holes

A cat can struggle out of a cardboard box if the box isn't tied up properly. The box may also fall apart if it rains.

The collar must have some elastic so the cat has a chance to wriggle free if the collar gets caught.

Disc or tube for your name and address.

A collar like this will help to stop the cat getting lost. Get the cat used to the collar before you go on a journey.

Cats are sometimes less frightened in wire baskets because they can see what is going on. They get plenty of air too.

Inside the basket

newspaper

newspaper

If you go on a long journey, use a large box or basket so the cat has plenty of room to move around inside. You may need to give the cat some food and water on the journey.

Holidays

When you go on holiday, your cat will want to stay at home.

Some catteries put several cats together. Some give your cat its own area.

You may be able to get a neighbour or friend to come in every day to feed your cat and check that it is safe and well. If you can't do this, or if you are going away for more than a week or so, take your cat to a cattery. Choose one well before you go away as the good ones are usually very busy at holiday time.

The people at the cattery will check that your cat is healthy before they let it stay. They may ask for vaccination certificates (see page 45).

Moving house

If you move to a new home, make a fuss of your cat. Make sure its own toys and bowls are easy for it to find. As your cat gets older, it will be more upset by moving and take longer to settle in.

Keep your cat indoors for a few days until it gets to know the new home. Then let it out to explore just before mealtimes. It will soon come back to eat rather than going too far away and getting lost.

Your cat's health

A healthy cat looks alert, with bright eyes and a clean, glossy coat. It eats well and spends a lot of time washing and grooming. If you see a change in the way your cat looks, eats, drinks or sleeps this could mean it isn't feeling well. Sickness, diarrhoea, coughing and sneezing can be signs of illness.

Chewing grass

Cats will eat grass sometimes. This can make them vomit and helps them to get rid of balls of fur in their stomach. Town cats that don't have a garden or yard should have their own patch of grass in a window box or flower pot.

Small animals, such as fleas, mites or worms may live on your cat's skin or inside its body. They may make the cat feel ill.

Fleas

Fleas can live on a cat's skin. If your cat has fleas, it will scratch its body a lot. Brush the cat over a pale surface. Then take the cat away and sprinkle water on the surface. If red specks appear, your cat has fleas. Buy some flea powder and follow the instructions. Clean the cat's bed and the carpets thoroughly.

Ear Mites

Mites can live in the wax inside a cat's ear. The cat will scratch its ears and shake its head. Don't touch the ears as they are very delicate. Take the cat to a vet.

Worms

All kittens should be given a medicine for roundworms. Adult cats may get tapeworms. Go to your vet for medicines.

Going to the vet

The vet can give your cat injections that will help to stop it getting some serious illnesses. This is called "vaccination". Ask your vet about vaccinations while your cat is still a kitten. If you think your cat is ill or has been injured, ask an adult to help you take it to the vet. Some diseases can kill a cat in just a few days.

When your cat is ill, put it gently in its travelling box and take it to the vet. If the cat tries to scratch or bite you, ask an adult to help you wrap it in a blanket or towel.

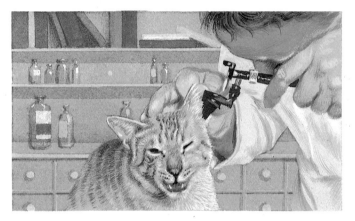

The vet will examine your cat and tell you what is wrong. This cat has something in its ears. Ask the vet how to look after your cat at home when it is ill.. Let the cat rest quietly.

Giving pills or medicine

Often the vet will give you pills or medicine to give your cat at home.

It isn't easy to give pills or medicine to cats. You can try mixing a crushed pill or some medicine with the cats' food but they often won't eat it.

Ask your vet how to give pills to a cat. Don't do this by yourself. An adult must help you otherwise you may get bitten.

45

Cats and kittens

A female cat can start having kittens when she is about six months old. She could have three litters every year with up to six kittens in each litter.

It is very difficult to find good homes for so many kittens. It is best to take your cat to the vet when she is about six months old to have an operation called spaying. This will stop her having kittens.

Vets will shave the area where they operate.

A male cat should have an operation called neutering when he is about six months old. This will stop him being the father of any kittens. A neutered cat is usually quieter and more home-loving.

Some male cats get fatter after they are neutered.

If a female cat is **not** spayed, she will behave strangely from time to time. She will call for a male in a loud, wailing voice. She will also rub against things to leave her scent for a male cat.

A female cat may roll on the ground to attract a male cat.

If a male cat is **not** neutered, he often spends a lot of time out of doors. He may fight other male cats and come home dirty and perhaps wounded. He will leave a strong scent in the house.

The male cat that wins the fight may mate with the female.

When your cat has kittens

After a female cat has mated, baby kittens may start to form inside her. This is called being pregnant. Don't pick her up unless you have to and handle her very gently.

If your cat is pregnant, her nipples will be swollen and pinker than usual.

Her tummy will get larger as the kittens grow inside her.

A pregnant cat will become very hungry and needs much more food. She may also need cod-liver oil and extra vitamins.

Your cat will be ready to give birth about nine weeks after mating. She will look for a warm, safe place to make a nest.

Cats are good mothers and do not usually need help when they give birth. It is best to watch from nearby so you can call the vet if there any problems. As soon as they are born, the kittens crawl to their mother's nipples to suck milk. Don't handle the kittens until their eyes are open.

Put out a cardboard box and line it with old, clean towels or newspaper. Your cat might use it.

Low entrance for mother and kittens.

47

Picture puzzle

There are 13 cats hidden in this picture.
Can you find them all?

DOGS AND PUPPIES

Shetland
Sheepdog

Watch the dog run

Hold the
Dog pages
like this.

Watch the top right hand
corner and flick the pages
over fast.

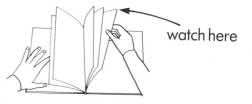

watch here

Being a dog owner

A dog will become a member of your family. There are some important things for you and your parents to think about before your family gets a dog. You will need your parents' help to look after it and train it.

Dogs live for about 14 years. A dog needs looking after every day of its life. You will have to feed it, take it for walks, play with it and groom it.

This dog is waiting to go for its evening walk.

This dog has been left alone for too long. It is making a noise because it is unhappy. Your neighbours may complain.

Dogs like company so much that they must not be left alone for more than a few hours.

Take your dog for its walks at about the same time every day.

Irish Setter

Owning a dog costs money. You will need money to buy the dog, to buy a collar, lead and basket. You will have to buy food and pay for vet's bills, and for kennels when you go away on holiday.

Bearded Collie

Your parents may need to put up a strong high fence round the garden, to stop the dog escaping.

German Shepherd Dog

Dog owners have laws to obey. You must buy a name and address tag and a licence for your dog. In some countries, your dog must wear a licence tag on its collar, and a tag to say that it has been vaccinated against rabies.

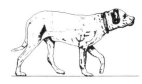

You must keep your dog on a lead on the roads, and in most public places.

If your dog is loose and runs into the road, it may cause an accident. This can cost the dog owner a lot of money.

A dog needs a lot of looking after and training. But with care and affection it will become a loyal friend, ready to join in with your games.

Sheep are frightened of dogs, and can even be killed by them. A farmer may shoot a dog if it is a nuisance. You may be fined if your dog chases farm animals.
You may also be fined if your dog fouls footpaths and you can get into trouble if your dog bites someone.

51

Choosing a dog

These pages will help you choose what kind of dog you want. There are about 200 breeds of dog. You can see some of them in this part of the book. Read other books about them, and talk to dog owners you know.

Big dogs are very strong. They need a lot of space in the house and garden, and a big open space nearby for walks. They need a lot of food as well as exercise.

Afghan Hound

Yorkshire Terrier

Small dogs need less food and space, but they can be quite fierce.

Long-haired dogs need a lot of regular grooming.

Old English Sheepdog

This dog's coat needs clipping – it can't see!

A big dog can knock you down even when it is being friendly.

Some dogs are bred for their looks rather than for the way they behave. So you should find out as much as possible about your favourite breed. Ask your local vet for advice, and talk to local breeders.

A mongrel is a mixture of breeds. Mongrels are often very good-natured, and they are cheaper to buy than pedigree dogs.

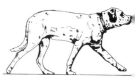

You won't know how big a mongrel puppy will grow, even if you see the mother.

This little puppy...

grew to this size!

Choosing a puppy

Once you have decided what kind of dog you would like, find a breeder or a private home where puppies are for sale, or ask at an animal welfare organization. If the puppies are pedigreed, ask your local vet for advice on the breed.

The owner should let you see the puppies with their mother. Choose a healthy puppy that is friendly, alert, playful and interested in you. It mustn't be too fat or too thin. It should have bright eyes, and a clean coat, ears and nose.

Jack Russell

Your puppy's new home

Before you bring your puppy home, you will need quite a few things for it. It's nice to choose a name for the puppy so that you can start using its name as soon as you bring it home.

West Highland White Terrier

Safe toys to play with.

When you collect the puppy, you should take a strong box with you, lined with newspaper. The puppy will never have been on a lead, and it will be safer and happier tucked up in a box.

At first everything will seem strange and frightening for your puppy. Welcome it with some food and water and stroke it gently. Don't give it too many new people to meet.

Your dog must have its own bed. Give your puppy a box rather than an expensive bed, as the puppy may tear or chew it up. The bed must be away from draughts and damp. (You can raise it off the floor on piles of magazines.)

The bed must be big enough for the dog to curl up in comfortably.

Line the bed with a washable blanket on top of newspaper.

Leave plenty of newspaper around the bed.

Cocker Spaniel

Puppies may cry on their first few nights with you, because they miss sleeping with their brothers, sisters and mother. Don't go to your puppy every time it cries. If you do, it will cry whenever you leave it.

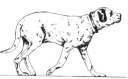

You could give your puppy a warm hot water bottle wrapped in a cloth, and a ticking clock for company.

Your puppy will soon stop being afraid. It will rush around exploring and licking everything it can – including you!

Beagle

Puppy collars

Your puppy will need a puppy collar and lead. The collar should be loose enough for two fingers to fit inside, when the puppy is wearing it.

elastic

Puppy collar.

Disc with your address on.

As your dog grows, it will need a bigger and stronger collar and lead.

Contact your local vet at once. Your puppy may need worming and vaccinations against illnesses before it is 3 months old.

Handling a puppy

When you pick up a puppy, always use both hands. Do not pick it up under its stomach or by its front legs.

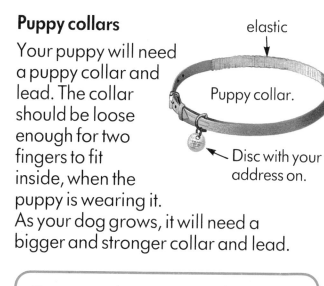

One hand supports the front legs.

The other supports the back legs.

Hold it firmly, but not tightly, to stop it jumping down. Never try to pick up a big dog.

Feeding dogs and puppies

In the wild, dogs have to search or hunt for food, so they eat as much as possible when they find food. Pet dogs will do the same, but it is not kind to let your dog eat too much at once, or to leave it for too long without feeding.

Feeding puppies

Young puppies need 4 meals a day at first, since their stomachs are quite small. You can feed yours on mixtures of canned, semi-moist, dried or fresh meat, biscuits, cereals and milk. You should always leave it fresh water. When your puppy is 3 months old, it can have 3 bigger meals a day. By 6 months it will only need 2 larger meals. Make the meals bigger by adding more meat and biscuits but less milk. By 9 months, most dogs do well on one meal a day.

Feeding adult dogs

Adult dogs do well on mixtures of meats, cereals and biscuits. Canned, semi-moist or dried food is easy to give, together with biscuits and water. The amount your dog needs depends on its size. You can get advice about this from vets or dog breeders. Feed your dog at the same time, and in the same place every day. Dogs need water at all times.

West Highland White Terrier

As puppies get older, they need bigger meals but less often.

When you feed your puppy **canned or dried foods,** it is best to use the ones made for puppies. When you feed your puppy **fresh foods,** it will need a mixture of meat, cereal and warm milk. The meat can be red or white meat and it should all be finely chopped. Cereals are things like porridge, brown bread or puppy meal. Ask your vet for advice about how to make up a balanced diet for your dog.

If you watch your dog eating, you will see that it doesn't chew its food. Adult dogs have big stomachs which can take large lumps of food. They need to rest after a meal in order to digest their food.

Great Dane

Tall dogs need their bowls raised off the floor.

Bloodhound

Dogs with long ears need small bowls with steep sides.

Chocolate Labrador

Dogs love bones. Bones are good for their teeth and gums. But only give your dog big, raw marrow bones. Chicken bones and other small sharp bones are dangerous.

Dogs are greedy. Don't feed your dog with titbits between meals or when you are eating. Too many sweet things are bad for your dog.

Black Labrador

Dogs may steal food even if they aren't hungry.

In the house

Sleeping

Pet dogs usually live indoors. Your dog must have a bed of its own. Once your dog is fully grown, you can buy it a new bed. There are many different kinds of bed for dogs. The one you choose must be big enough for the dog to turn round in, and easy enough to clean.

Cavalier
King Charles
Spaniel

Dogs sleep for about 14 hours each day. Puppies sleep for even longer.

Yellow
Labrador

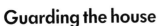

The bed is your dog's own place in the house. It may hide its favourite toys or bones there, and will go there when it wants to be by itself.

Afghan
Hound

Guarding the house

Bulldog

Any breed which lives and sleeps indoors and which barks at sudden noises will help to guard the house.

Dogs often like sleeping on hard surfaces, especially when it is warm or sunny. They may stretch out to enjoy it.

Toilet training

At 8 weeks old, a puppy may make 12 puddles a day! But puppies soon learn not to make a mess in the house. Your puppy is most likely to want to go to the lavatory when it wakes up, and after each meal or drink. When it wants to go, it will probably sniff the floor and circle round. Put your puppy outside at these times, and praise it when it manages to go to the lavatory outside.

If you catch it making a puddle inside, say "No!" firmly. Don't shout or hit your puppy. It will know by the tone of your voice that it has done wrong. Clean up any mess properly. Wash your hands afterwards.

Put your puppy outside when it wants to go to the lavatory.

Cocker Spaniel

Another way of toilet training is to make the puppy go to the lavatory on newspaper. Start off with lots of sheets on the floor. Gradually take bits away until you have just one sheet by the door. Then move the sheet into the garden. Your puppy should then learn to ask to go out.

Be careful, especially when your dog is a puppy, not to leave small or sharp objects lying around – your puppy could swallow them. Plastic bags are also dangerous – your puppy could suffocate inside one. Protect electric flex – your puppy could bite through it to the live wire. Don't leave your toys and slippers around with the puppy if you don't want them chewed up!

Cairn Terrier

Playing

Dalmatian

Puppies love to play with anything. They learn things and get exercise from playing. But they do less damage if they have their own toys.

If you buy a ball, it must be the right size for your dog. It must be big enough not to get swallowed. Balls or other toys made of soft rubber are dangerous. The dog may chew them and swallow the rubber.

If you play with sticks, make sure they are not sharp or have nails sticking out. Never throw stones, as your dog may swallow them or hurt its teeth.

Some dogs like to play hide and seek. Make your dog sit while you hide a toy, and then let the dog look for the toy.

Some dogs enjoy swimming. You can throw sticks into the water for them to fetch.

Munsterlander

Many dogs enjoy fetching and bringing. If you throw a stick, they will fetch it, and bring it back to you. This is fun and good exercise for your dog.

This dog is asking someone to play with it.

Some dogs enjoy playing tug-of-war. But be careful that your dog does not damage its teeth or hurt its mouth.

Sometimes when dogs play together, they can look as though they are fighting.

German Shepherd Dog

Some dogs like jumping for things. But don't make your dog jump too high or it might hurt itself.

Looking after your dog

Exercise

Adult dogs need to be taken for a walk outside. Start taking your dog out on the lead while it is still young. You must train it to come when you call before you can let it off the lead (see pages 64 - 65).

German Shepherd Dog

Dogs like to run freely and explore. They like to sniff different scents and meet other dogs. A short walk and run off the lead in a safe place is much better than a long walk on the lead.

English Setter

Puppies get all the exercise they need from playing at home and in the garden. They shouldn't be allowed beyond the garden until they have been vaccinated.

Collars and leads

You will need to choose the right collar and lead for your dog. The pet store assistant should be able to help you.

Dobermann

Correct way   Wrong way

Sometimes a choke chain lead (see pictures) is used as a training aid. This type of lead can hurt a dog and must be used carefully. A choke chain should not normally be used in place of an ordinary collar and lead.

Bassett Hound

A male dog will mark out its trail on a walk by urinating on things it passes such as lampposts or trees. By doing this it leaves its scent. It will also sniff the trails of other dogs who have left their scents. Each dog has its own scent.

Grooming

You should brush or comb your dog's coat regularly to keep it clean and healthy.

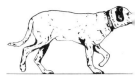

Short-haired dogs only need brushing. You can use an old soft hairbrush.

Long-haired dogs need combing as well as brushing, every day.

St Bernard

Washing

If your dog rubs itself in smelly things like cow pats you may have to give it a bath.

Miniature Poodle

You can bath a small dog in the sink, but large dogs will have to be done in the garden with a watering can or hose. Always use warm water and a special dog shampoo. Rinse it well. Dry it with its own towel, and keep it warm afterwards. You should dry your dog after a walk in the rain too.

Training your dog

The best way to train your dog is to let only one person (usually an adult) be in charge of the lessons. Do them in an enclosed garden, or a space that the dog knows. Start when your dog is about six months old.

Always use a firm kind voice, and say only short simple words. Always say the words in the same way, and your dog will learn to recognize them quickly. Give it lots of praise every time it does the correct thing. Be patient and never lose your temper with your dog.

Regular, short lessons are much better than one long lesson. Train your dog for 5-10 minutes at a time, two or more times a day.

There are four basic things your dog should learn.

HEEL

First it should learn to walk to heel. Once the puppy has got used to a collar, attach a lead, and let the puppy run around by itself. Then hold the lead so that the puppy is just behind your left leg, with its head close to your leg. Say "heel" and begin to walk. If it tries to overtake you, or pulls away, pull it back to you firmly and say "heel" again. Praise it when it begins to walk in the correct position.

SIT

Then it should learn to sit. Let your dog stand still, then say "sit" and at the same time push down firmly on its behind, until it is forced into the sitting position. Praise it. Repeat this until the dog doesn't need you to press down at all, and sits just at your command.

Don't push down too hard. You might hurt the dog.

Labrador

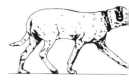

If your dog is well-trained, both of you will be able to enjoy yourselves more. You will be able to do more together because you know your dog will obey your commands at a time when it may be dangerous.

STAY

Sometimes you will want your dog to stay in the same sitting position. Once it has learned to sit, say "stay" and take a few steps backwards. Your dog will try to follow you. Say "stay" again and make it sit. Keep praising it when it stays sitting, and gradually it will learn to stay.

Golden Retriever

COME

Lastly, you must be able to call your dog to you. This is an important lesson. By now your dog should know its name. Attach a long piece of string to the lead, and make your dog sit. Then say "stay" and walk backwards a few steps. Then say "come" and call the dog's name. At the same time, pull gently but firmly on the string. Praise the dog when it comes to you.

Gradually walk farther backwards until you have let all the string out. After a few lessons you should be able to call the dog to you without using the lead.

Travelling

Most dogs love car journeys. But sometimes puppies are travel sick on their first few journeys, so it's best to keep these short. Some dogs become restless on journeys. Your dog must learn to sit still.

Samoyed

Some cars have room to keep your dog at the back behind a wire guard.

On long journeys, take fresh water and your dog's bowl so that you can give it a drink when it gets thirsty. If you are driving, stop now and then and let your dog out on its lead.

You should not allow your dog to hang its head out of the window when the car is moving. This is dangerous for the dog, and may hurt its eyes.

English Springer Spaniel

You musn't leave a puppy alone inside a parked car, even for a few minutes. Don't leave an adult dog alone in the car if you can avoid it. If you do it will become very unhappy. If you must leave your dog in the car, make sure the car is parked in the shade. Never leave a dog in the car if it is very hot or very cold.

You should have at least two windows wide enough open to let fresh air in, but not so wide that the dog can get out through them.

On holiday

When you take your dog on holiday, it may take a while to settle in. A country dog may be frightened by town traffic and noises. A town dog may get very excited in the country and might start chasing farm animals. Always keep your dog on a lead at first. To help your dog settle in, take along its bed and feeding bowls.

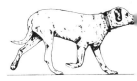

Golden Retriever

Some dogs enjoy swimming and playing in water. Call your dog back before it swims off too far, or annoys other people. Don't let your dog swim in rivers with a strong current.

At the beach, you should bring fresh water and your dog's bowl. If it drinks sea water, it may be sick. Never let your dog go to the lavatory on the beach.

Boarding kennels

If it's impossible for your dog to come with you on holiday, and if there is no one to look after it, you could take the dog to boarding kennels. You will need to book a place for the dog before you go away, and you will have to show its vaccination certificate.

If you move house, your dog might be happier in kennels while you are moving.

Most dogs are happy in kennels once their owners are out of sight.

Your dog's health

If your dog suddenly starts behaving in a strange way, it may be ill. Dogs will often vomit (be sick). Sometimes they eat grass to help themselves vomit. But if your dog doesn't want to eat for more than two days, or keeps on vomiting or having diarrhoea, it may be seriously ill. You should take it to the vet.

Worms

If your dog seems to be much more hungry than usual, and yet it seems to be getting thinner, it may have worms. All dogs, especially puppies, need medicine for worms regularly. Your vet will give you some worm pills.

Cavalier King Charles Spaniel

Scratching

If your dog scratches a lot, or bites its skin, it's probably trying to get rid of an itch. You should take it to the vet. He may say that grooming will help. Or your dog may have fleas. The vet will give you some flea spray or powder. If your dog shakes its head a lot, or scratches around the ears, you should take it to the vet. Ears are very delicate.

Chow Chow

Dogs often cut their paws. Always clean up cuts, and bandage them if necessary. If your dog gets a bad wound, you should take it to the vet.

Rabies is a disease which kills people. It can be caught from dogs with the disease if they bite you. In countries where rabies is found, dogs must be vaccinated against it. In other countries, such as Britain, where rabies isn't found, it is against the law to bring dogs in from abroad unless they go into quarantine.

Mating

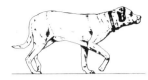

A female dog is called a bitch. She can have puppies from the age of about six months. Twice a year she will be "in season" and will be ready to mate with a male dog and have puppies. You can tell when your bitch is coming into season. You will see spots of blood around her hindquarters. She will become very attractive to male dogs.

Male dogs can smell these changes in female dogs. They may come and sniff her. If you don't want your bitch to have puppies, you must guard her closely when she is in season. Keep her on the lead when you take her out.

Male dogs may try to run away to mate with your dog. Sometimes they wait outside a bitch's house for days. Keep your bitch indoors when she is in season.

But the best thing to do if you don't want your bitch to have puppies is to have her neutered. Your vet can do this by a simple operation when she is five months old. This is kinder than having unwanted puppies destroyed.

Foxhound

Having puppies

If you do want your dog to have puppies, and you know that they will go to good homes, you should find a mate of the same breed for her. You must give your dog extra care for 9 weeks after the mating, and for a month or two after the birth. When your dog is pregnant, take it to the vet for a check up.

West Highland White Terrier

After your bitch has mated, puppies may start to form inside her. This is called being "pregnant". You will notice her tummy and nipples begin to swell. She will become less playful. She must be given plenty of milk, less cereal and more meat. Start giving her extra food 3 weeks before the puppies are due.

Two weeks before her puppies are due (about 7 weeks after mating) line your dog's bed with newspaper. She may tear it up to make a nest. Just before she gives birth, your bitch will seem restless. She will go to her nest. She needs to be left in peace, but with someone nearby.

A puppy is born in a sac, which the mother chews open to free the puppy, before the next one is born. The mother licks each puppy clean. There may be as many as 10 puppies if your dog is large. A smaller dog has 4-6 puppies.

Dachshund

Puppies are blind and deaf when they are born. They begin to see and hear at about 8 days old. They cannot walk, but use their front legs to drag themselves along.

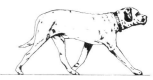

The mother will need extra food while the puppies are feeding on her milk. By the time the pups are 3 weeks old, she may need 3 times as much as usual.

Rough Collie

You should try not to touch the puppies for about two weeks after they are born. You may upset their mother. She may try to protect them, even from people she knows.

At 3 weeks old, the puppies can walk. They will leave the nest and begin to explore. At this time you should start to feed the puppies small meals. You can buy special puppy food.

A puppy will probably walk into a saucer of food before it learns to eat from it.

Beagle

71

Picture puzzle

There are 13 dogs hidden in this picture.
Can you find them all?

SMALL PETS

Watch the rat jump

Hold the Small pets pages like this.

Watch the top right hand corner and flick the pages over fast.

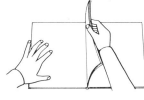

watch here

Being a small pet owner

This part of the book is about how to look after **budgerigars, gerbils, hamsters, mice, rats, guinea pigs** and **rabbits**. Budgerigars are sometimes called budgies or parakeets and guinea pigs are also called cavies. All these small pets are fairly easy to look after. When they are tame, they are interesting to watch and be with.

Before you get a small pet

You should ask your parents before you get a small pet. You will need their help to look after it.

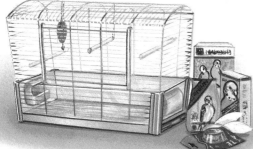

Small pets do not cost much to buy but you will have to spend money on food, cages or hutches and vet's bills.

How long do they live for?

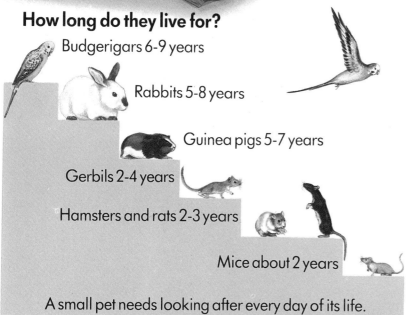

Budgerigars 6-9 years

Rabbits 5-8 years

Guinea pigs 5-7 years

Gerbils 2-4 years

Hamsters and rats 2-3 years

Mice about 2 years

A small pet needs looking after every day of its life.

Rabbits and guinea pigs need a garden for grazing and exercise.

You will have to spend some time every day handling your pet, feeding it, washing food and water containers and clearing out dirty hay or sawdust.

Most small pets should be kept with others of the same kind so they will not get lonely. Don't keep males and females together as they may produce a lot of babies. Hamsters must be kept on their own or they will fight.

If you go away for more than a day, you must make sure someone else looks after your small pet. Tell the person what to feed your pet and how to get in touch with the vet.

Dogs and cats frighten small pets. Keep your pet well out of reach of these larger pets and never leave them alone with a cat or a dog. They may die of fright, even in their own cages.

Small pets in schools

Small pets are sometimes kept in schools with a teacher's help. They must have someone to feed them and clean out their cages.

School pets need to be looked after at weekends and in the holidays as well.

Gerbils

75

Choosing a small pet

Before you choose a small pet, find out as much as possible about the different kinds that you can buy and make sure you know how to look after them properly. Your local animal welfare society will be able to give you information and advice. You could also talk to anyone in your area who breeds small pets.

Budgerigars

Wild budgies live in large groups, called flocks. Pet budgies like to be kept with other budgies but it is easier to teach a bird to talk if you keep it on its own.

There are more than 70 different colour patterns on pet budgies. They all make good pets, so choose the colours you like.

Gerbils

Gerbils are clean, busy animals that dig burrows. They are active in the day and at night and have long, furry tails.

Gerbils are curious and interested in what goes on around them.

Hamsters

Hamsters are clean and can become very tame. They usually sleep in the day and wake up at night. They have short tails and cheek pouches to carry food in.

This hamster is filling its pouches with food. It will store the food to eat later.

Mice

Mice are timid animals but are easy to tame. They are usually active at night. They may be difficult to hold as they are small. Their cages need to be cleaned out two or three times a week. There are lots of different coloured mice, all of which make good pets.

The long, scaly tail helps the mouse to climb.

Rats

Rats are playful and intelligent and like to learn tricks. They make interesting pets. They are often more active at night. There are only a few colours of rat for you to choose from.

A hooded rat

Pet rats are very clean animals.

Guinea pigs

Guinea pigs are timid, gentle and easy to hold and tame. They don't have a tail and cannot climb very well. Their hutches need cleaning out two or three times a week.

Long-haired ones need a lot of attention.

Rough-haired

Smooth-haired

Rabbits

Rabbits can soon become tame and friendly. They get bored easily so they need things to gnaw on and plenty of exercise. Some rabbits can be kept with guinea pigs.

Some rabbits are too big to pick up. The Dutch rabbit is a good size for you to hold.

Buying a small pet

You can buy a small pet from a friend, a good pet store or a breeder. A breeder will be able to tell you exactly how old your small pet is and who its parents and relations are. You can find a breeder by looking at advertisements in newspapers or magazines.

You can buy most small pets when they are about 6-12 weeks old. Make sure the pets you buy are healthy. Their fur or feathers should be clean, smooth and shiny and their eyes should be bright. They should be alert and interested in you. Check that they can move properly.

Watch a budgie fly and eat. Its feathers should be glossy and close to the body.

An adult male budgie has blue above his beak.

nostril

An adult female has brown above her beak.

A young budgie has stripes on its head, no white ring around its eyes and no clear throat spots.

A healthy rabbit's ears should move in the direction of small sounds and its nose should be twitching.

The mouse you buy should have a long, pointed tail.

This healthy mouse has bright eyes and ears that stand up.

Hamsters wake up in the evening. They may not look alert in the day, even if they are healthy.

Taking your small pet home

lots of air holes

hay inside the box

You will need a box or cage to carry your small pet home in. Make sure it is tightly shut and carry it carefully.

Teeth

Gerbils, hamsters, mice, rats, guinea pigs and rabbits all have sharp front teeth. Use a strong box or cage to carry them in so that they can't gnaw their way out and escape.

Homes — part 1

Before you bring your small pets home, you must buy or make a cage or hutch for them to live in. Small pets spend most of their lives in cages or hutches so they need to be as large as possible. Put your small pets' home off the ground and away from draughts and direct sun.

Budgerigars

Indoor cages must be large enough for the birds to hop and stretch their wings. Two birds must have more room than one. Birds don't like smoky rooms

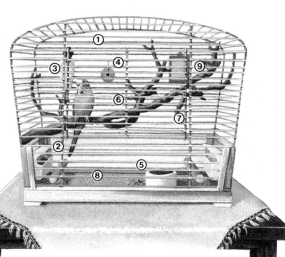

① Horizontal bars for climbing
② Seed and water dishes
③ Cuttlefish "bone"
④ Mineral block
⑤ Grit dish
⑥ Branch from a fruit tree. This helps the budgie to exercise its feet and trim its beak.
⑦ Door that can be left open when the bird is out.
　⑧ Sand on the floor helps to trim the budgie's claws and keep the cage clean.
⑨ Toys, such as a mirror

plenty of perches

warm, dry sleeping area

The best home for budgies is a large, outdoor aviary like this. Many budgies can live together as they do in the wild. There is more room for them to fly than in a small cage indoors. But you will need a lot of space for an aviary and it also costs a lot to build one.

Gerbils, hamsters, mice and rats

Young Hooded rat →

Gerbils should have plenty of soil or sawdust to burrow in. The best sort of home for them is a large fish tank with peat and straw inside (see page 75).

Rats, mice and gerbils like to climb on ladders and branches in the cage. You could use a branch from a fruit tree.

Gerbils, hamsters or mice can live in a cage like the one in the picture below. Rats need a cage three or four times bigger than this. Metal cages are cold and get rusty. Wooden cages are warmer than metal ones but make sure you use a strong wood, otherwise your pets may gnaw their way out.

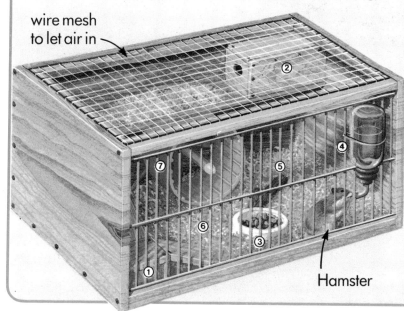

wire mesh to let air in

Hamster

① Ramps, shelves and ladders to give your pet room to move and play.
② Wooden nesting box
③ Heavy food dish
④ Water bottle
⑤ Something hard to gnaw on. This will help to stop the teeth growing too long.
⑥ Lots of coarse sawdust to absorb droppings and help to keep the animals warm.
⑦ Solid wheel for exercise

Homes — part 2

Guinea pigs and rabbits live in hutches. They should be made of strong wood and have good hinges and catches. The hutch can be outdoors but should be out of draughts and direct sun. If the weather gets very cold, move the hutch into a dry, airy shed. Don't keep a hutch in a garage as car fumes are poisonous.

Sloping roof so that rain runs off.

Warm, dry sleeping area

Living area with plenty of room for the rabbit to move around. Newspaper and sawdust on the floor.

Hay rack so the rabbit doesn't trample on its food.

Door made of solid wood.

water bottle

Hay and sawdust for the rabbit to sleep on.

mineral block

Long legs to keep out damp from the ground. This will also stop other animals from getting in and make cleaning easier.

Heavy **food dish** that won't tip over.

Log or branch for the rabbit to gnaw on. This will help to stop its teeth growing too long.

Door made of wire netting.

Guinea pigs and rabbits need an outdoor pen for exercise. Keep the pen out of direct sun and wind and away from poisonous plants. Rabbits need a wire mesh floor or they may burrow out.

The pen should have food and water inside.

Heap of hay to play or hide in.

Cleaning cages and hutches

Buy a cage or hutch that is easy to clean rather than a pretty one. Dirty cages or hutches can make your pet ill. You should wash food and water containers and clean out dirty hay or sawdust every day. Some small pets may use one corner of their home as a lavatory and this makes cleaning easier.

Wash the cage or hutch at least once a week if possible. Guinea pigs and mice will need cleaning out more often. Use a mild soap and hot water and rinse it many times. Make sure it is completely dry before you put anything back.

slide-out tray →

← Put your pet in another cage, pen or box while you clean its home.

83

Feeding – part 1

Small pets need good food to grow strong and healthy. Make sure the food is clean. Wash the vegetables and fruit to get rid of any chemical sprays that the farmer may have used. Always feed your pets fresh food. Stale food can make them ill. They enjoy different tastes so give them a mixture of different foods.

Food bowls must be heavy so they cannot be tipped over easily. They should be washed every day.

All small pets need fresh drinking water every day. Bottles are better than dishes for water. The water in a dish may get dirty or be tipped out. Check that the bottle works properly and make sure it is always clean and full of water.

Here are some of the wild plants that you can feed to your small pet. Be careful to pick the right ones as some wild plants are poisonous.

Clover

Groundsel

Dandelion

Chickweed

Give your pets some greens to nibble during the day. You can feed them things like lettuce, water cress, spinach, carrot or apple as well as **some** wild plants.

Small pets can have treats sometimes. Treats can be raisins, nuts, sunflower seeds or small dog biscuits. Chocolates and sweets are not treats. They may make some small pets very ill.

Budgerigars

Wild budgies eat grass seeds and some green plants. You can buy budgie seed from pet stores and supermarkets. Budgies have no teeth so they need to eat some grit. The grit helps them to grind up their food.

Budgies crack seeds open with their strong beak. They swallow the middle of the seed and drop the outer shell, which is called the husk. The husk often lands on top of the other seeds in their food dish. You will need to blow any husks away so the birds can reach the whole seeds underneath.

grit dish

Budgies like to eat some seed all through the day. Top up the dish once a day.

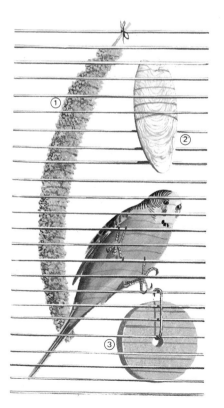

① Hang a spray of millet seed in the cage once a week. Don't leave it there all the time.

② Budgies need a cuttlefish "bone" to give them some calcium. They can also trim their beaks on the cuttlefish.

③ You should also hang a mineral block in the cage where the budgie can peck at it.

Put treats in a special treat cup twice a week. Give your budgie some greens and grate up any carrot or apple.

85

Feeding – part 2

Gerbils

Gerbils should be fed mainly on dry grains such as oats, maize, barley and wheat. You can buy a balanced mixture of grains from good pet stores or supermarkets. Treats can be sunflower seeds or cornflakes. Gerbils can also have tiny amounts of fresh greens. You can put a small grass turf in their cage.

Hamsters

The best time to feed your hamster is in the evening. You can buy a grain mixture in good pet stores or supermarkets. Give your hamster plenty of fresh greens every day as well but don't feed it onions, oranges or lemons. You can also make up a mash of table scraps sometimes. Ask your vet for advice.

Gerbils use their front paws to hold their food. If you give your pet some food by hand, it will help to make it tame.

Hamsters use their front paws to take food in and out of their cheek pouches. Don't give them oats in husks as they are spiky and may scratch the pouches.

Hamsters make a store of food in one part of their cage. When you clean out the cage, put the store of food back unless it is stale or going mouldy.

Mice and rats

Mice and rats eat the same sort of food and like a lot of small meals every day. Rats need more food than mice. Give them grain mixtures from good pet stores or supermarkets. They can have fresh greens two or three times a week. Treats can be cheese, apple or carrot.

Guinea pigs and rabbits

Guinea pigs and rabbits need two meals a day. Give them pellets and a mixture of grains from good pet stores or supermarkets. They should also have plenty of fresh greens such as carrot or cabbage. To give them a change, you can make up a mash of food soaked in milk or water. Ask your vet or animal welfare society for advice. These small pets need fresh hay every day as well as their meals.

Rabbits

Guinea pigs are greedy. They will get fat if they don't have enough exercise. They need food that is rich in vitamin C (such as cabbage or apple) or they may become ill.

Mice eating grain mixture

Taming and handling

Small pets can soon become tame if they get used to being handled while they are still young. Be patient at first and don't frighten your pet. Talk quietly so that it gets used to your voice.

When your pet has been at home for a few days, you can get it used to being handled. Make sure your pet is awake and knows you are there. Move your hand slowly towards the animal and let it sniff you. Don't make any sudden, jerky movements or you may get bitten. When your pet is no longer frightened of your hand, you can pick it up.

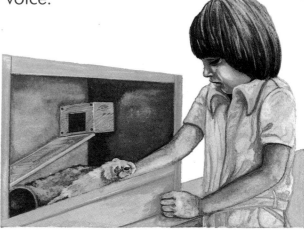

Budgerigars

When the budgie knows your hand, put your finger next to its perch. Wait until it hops onto your finger. Then move your hand slowly in the cage and talk quietly. After a week or so, carry the bird out of the cage and let it fly (see page 90).

When you pick up a budgie, hold it like this. Don't pick it up unless you have to and handle the bird very gently or you may hurt it. Ask an adult to help you.

Gerbils, hamsters, mice, rats, guinea pigs and rabbits

Once these small pets are tame, they need to be handled every day. Don't handle them for too long or they will get tired. Hold them firmly but gently. Never squeeze your pet or you may hurt it.

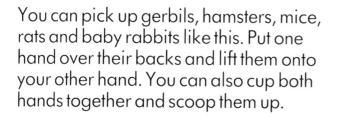

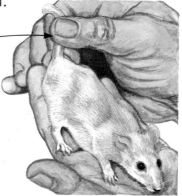

Hold the tail here. Never pick up your pet by the tip of its tail.

You can pick up gerbils, hamsters, mice, rats and baby rabbits like this. Put one hand over their backs and lift them onto your other hand. You can also cup both hands together and scoop them up.

A gerbil or mouse can be picked up by the widest part of the tail. Then quickly slide your other hand under the animal's body to take the weight. Never let your pet hang by its tail.

Never lift a rabbit by its ears.

Put one hand under a guinea pig's body and use the other hand to support it. Let it rest or stand on one of your hands so that it feels safe.

Rabbits should be lifted in and out of the hutch backwards in case they jump or kick you. Hold the rabbit against you and use both arms to take its weight.

Exercise and play

Small pets need things to play with and plenty of exercise or they will be bored and unhappy. When your pet has settled in, get it used to being let out of the cage or hutch for a short time each day. Before you let it out, close any doors or windows and make sure there are no cats or dogs about.

When budgies are tame enough to perch on your finger, they can fly free in a room. To put the budgie back in its cage, hold your finger up and call quietly. When the bird lands on your finger, carry it back to the cage. If the budgie won't come back to you, make the room dark. The bird will not fly in the dark and you can then catch it.

You can put toys, such as mirrors or ladders, into your budgie's cage. Don't put too many toys in at once or the bird may not have room to move about.

Teaching budgies to talk

It may take many weeks or months to teach a budgie to talk. Start with its name and say the name clearly over and over again. Talk to your budgie whenever you are near it. It will repeat exactly what you say.

Some small pets will explore you all over once they get to know you.

Gerbils, hamsters, mice, rats, guinea pigs and rabbits love to explore and can move quickly. They must be watched all the time they are out of their cages or hutches. They may disappear through holes or narrow cracks or chew electric wires. You could give them a large cardboard box to play in so that you can see where they are.

Gerbils love to jump, burrow and climb.

Gerbils, hamsters, mice and rats like to play with tissue boxes, kitchen roll tubes, paper bags, milk cartons and nuts.

A wheel may help your pets to exercise but it must be a solid wheel. They may hurt their feet or tails in the spokes of an open wheel.

Turn a small box upside down to make a house for your guinea pig to play in. Cut a hole in the side for the door.

If you lose your gerbil, hamster, mouse or rat, you may be able to catch it by leaving some food in a large jar or tin on the floor. Once the pet has gone in to eat the food, it will be trapped.

Health

Small pets are more likely to be healthy if they are looked after properly. They should live in a large, clean, warm home, eat a balanced diet and have plenty of exercise and attention. Check your pet's health every day. Once you get to know your pet, you will notice when it isn't well.

If you think your pet is ill, ask an adult to help you take it to the vet. The vet will tell you how to nurse your pet at home. You will have to keep it warm and let it rest quietly. Make sure it has fresh food and water.

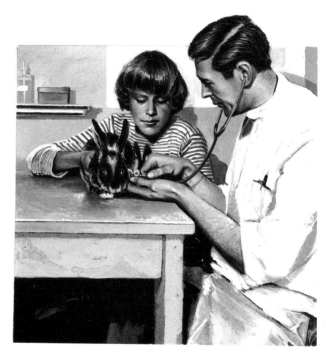

If a budgie is ill, it usually sits silently with its feathers puffed out like this. It may also sit like this if it is cold or tired.

If your pet has any small scratches or bites, ask an adult to put some mild antiseptic on them. But you must take your pet to a vet if it has a serious injury.

Rabbit paw

The teeth, claws or beaks of small pets may sometimes grow too long. A vet must trim them. The vet may show an adult how to do this.

Make sure you buy the right sort of powder or spray for your pet.

Parasites, such as fleas, ticks or lice may live on your pet's skin. You can buy a powder or spray to help to get rid of parasites. Ask an adult to help you and always follow the instructions exactly. You will have to clean your pet's home thoroughly as well.

Grooming and preening

Small pets groom or preen themselves and each other. This helps to keep their fur or feathers clean and healthy. It also helps them to get rid of parasites.

Most budgies enjoy splashing in a budgie bath or a saucer of water. This helps them to keep their feathers clean and healthy.

Short-haired guinea pigs and rabbits sometimes enjoy being groomed, especially when they are moulting. Long-haired guinea pigs have to be brushed every day. Brush in the same direction that the fur grows.

93

Small pets and their young

Small pets can have many babies every year. For example, a male and a female rat could produce up to 100 babies in one year. It is difficult to find good homes for all these young ones, so don't keep males and females together. It is possible for vets to operate on some pets to stop them being the mother or father of any babies. But this can be dangerous for small pets and they may die.

Breeding budgerigars

Breeders put budgie nest boxes in a large cage. Budgies do not make nests. The female lays 4-8 eggs in a hollow on the floor of the nest box. She lays one egg every other day. She sits on the eggs and turns them over from time to time. The male feeds the female whilst she sits on the eggs.

Both parents produce a thick, milky liquid to feed the chicks when they first hatch. The first chick is quite big by the time the last one hatches. When the chicks are older, their parents cough up food for them to eat.

When budgies hatch out, they have no feathers. They start to grow feathers after about a week.

Breeding gerbils, hamsters, mice, rats and rabbits

When these small pets are born, they have no fur and their eyes and ears are closed. They suck milk from their mother for the first few weeks. The nest must not be disturbed or the mother may kill the young. After a time, the young can go into their own cages.

These **hamsters** have just been born. They will start to grow fur after about a week.

Gerbils make good parents. A male and female stay together for life and both of them help to look after the young. Female hamsters and rabbits must be separated from the males after mating because they may fight each other.

Young rabbits have very short ears.

A female **rabbit** pulls out some of the soft fur from her stomach to line her nest. This helps to keep the babies warm. The mother quickly grows new fur. Female rabbits sometimes build fur nests even if they are not going to have babies.

Breeding guinea pigs

These guinea pigs have just been born. They are covered in fur and their eyes and ears are open. They will be able to run around after about an hour and will eat solid food after two days.

Picture Puzzle

There are 13 small pets hidden in this picture.
Can you find them all?

BIRDS

Games

1. Hunt the Grasshopper

Some birds eat Grasshoppers. Can you find 13 more Grasshoppers in the Bird pages?

2. Watch the bird fly

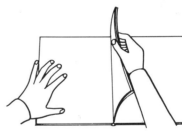

Hold the Bird pages like this.

Watch the top right hand corner and flick the pages over fast.

watch here

97

Looking at birds

A bird is like
an aeroplane.

Its shape helps it to
move fast through the air.

A bird is like
a bat.

It uses its arms
as wings.

Swallow

A bird is like
a weightlifter.
It has strong arm
and chest muscles.

A bird is like
a balloon.
It has lots of air
inside its body.

Birds are the only
animals in the world
that have feathers.

Birds have three kinds of feathers.

1. Down feathers.
They help keep the bird warm.

2. Body feathers.
They cover the body.

3. Flight feathers.
They help the bird to fly.

Greylag goose

Down feathers are under the body feathers.

body feathers

flight feathers

Birds grow a new set of feathers every year.

A goose cannot fly while its new flight feathers are growing.

baby goose

down feathers

Baby birds have down feathers to help keep them warm.

Taking off and flying

Bee-eater

Hummingbird

Wood Warbler

Blue Tit

When birds want to take off, they leap into the air and flap their wings as fast as they can.

Mute Swan

Some birds are too heavy to leap into the air. Before they can take off they have to run along flapping their wings.

Mallard

Tawny Owl

100

Eagles stretch out their
wide wings and float
on the air.

Golden Eagle

Large birds, like eagles, flap their wings slowly.
Small birds flap their wings very fast.

A wing is like an arm.
It bends in two places.

Common Tern

Kingfisher

Galah

Birds twist or bend their wings to turn in the air. Look at the
way the other birds on this page bend their wings.

Albatross

Goldfinch

101

Why do birds fly?

To build their nests in high places.

To go to warmer places where there is more food.

To catch food in the air.

To look for food on the ground.

To escape from their enemies.

Why do birds land?

To feed or rest in trees.

To feed on the ground.

To drink.

To rest.

To sit on their eggs.

To meet other birds and mate.

To feed their young.

Legs and feet

Birds walk on their toes.
They can run or hop
along the ground.

Puffin

A bird puts out its feet to land.
It also spreads out its tail and
wings to slow down.

A bird's leg
bends here.

Marabou Stork

Starling

This bird rests on branches.
When it bends its legs,
its toes lock on to the branch.

Some birds rest on the ground.
Storks often sit like this when they rest.

Birds often stand on one leg. They tuck the other leg under their feathers to keep it warm.

Coot

Mallard

Water birds have skin between their toes. The skin helps them to use their feet as paddles and to walk on mud without sinking in.

Snowy Owl

The feathers on its feet help it to walk on the snow without sinking in.

The Snowy Owl has claws like daggers. It kills with its feet. Its feet are covered with feathers to keep them warm.

Beaks and feeding

Birds have no teeth so they cannot chew food. They swallow food whole and then grind it up in their stomachs.

Kookaburra

Black Kite

This bird uses its hooked beak to tear up its food.

strainer

Shoveler

This duck uses its beak as a strainer. It collects tiny plants and animals from the top of the water.

Pelicans

pouch

A Pelican uses its huge beak to scoop fish from the water. Its beak can hold more food than its stomach.

Crossbill

Hummingbird

Rosella

Birds have different kinds of beaks because they eat different kinds of food. These seashore birds can feed close together because they eat different animals.

Godwits poke their beaks a short way into the mud to catch small animals.

Curlews have very long beaks. They eat animals that live deep in the mud.

Avocets sweep small animals off the top of the mud.

Turnstones catch small animals that live under stones or seaweed.

Oystercatchers open shellfish on rocks or in the mud.

Woodpecker

Splendid Wren

Barn Owl

Wigeon

107

Colours

Many birds match the colour of the leaves and branches of the trees they rest in. This helps them to hide from their enemies.

There are seven birds in this picture.
Can you see them all?

When birds are sitting on eggs, they need to be hidden. This female Nightjar is sitting on her eggs. She is hard to see.

Frogmouth

The Australian Frogmouth sleeps all day in a tree. It sits very still with its head up. It looks just like a broken branch.

Birds may use their colours to recognize each other.

Oystercatchers live together in big groups. If some of the birds fly off
to a new feeding place, the others soon follow. They recognize each other
by their colours and the calls that they make.

female

males

Male and female Mallards are different colours. Male Mallards are most colourful
in the breeding season. They show off their bright colours in a special dance.
This attracts a female for mating.

Song and dance

Birds sing most of all in the breeding season.

Male Blackbirds sing to attract female Blackbirds.

female Blackbird

Male Blackbirds also sing to tell other male Blackbirds "This is where I live so keep away".

Tawny Owls

Owls find each other in the dark by calling.

The male Pigeon has to dance in front of the female before he can mate with her. He turns in circles and "coos" loudly all the time.

1. The male makes himself look big. He puffs out his neck feathers.

female

male

2. He spreads out his tail like a fan and bows to the female.

female

male

Peacock

Peahen

The peacock uses his long feathers in a dance to attract a female. The long feathers fall out when the breeding season is over.

Eggs and nests

Soon after a female bird has mated, she lays her eggs. If she kept all her eggs inside her until they were ready to hatch, she would probably be too heavy to fly.

Guillemot eggs

Oystercatcher eggs

The female Common Tern lays her eggs on the ground. A baby Tern grows inside each egg.

The eggs match the colour of the ground around them. It is hard for enemies to see them.

When baby Terns hatch, they are covered with down. The down helps keep them warm.

If an enemy is about, the baby Terns crouch down so they are difficult to see.

Rook eggs

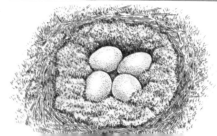

Eider Duck eggs

Most birds build nests. The nest hides the eggs and baby birds from enemies. It helps to keep them warm. Birds also sit on their eggs to keep them warm. If the eggs get cold, the baby birds inside them will die.

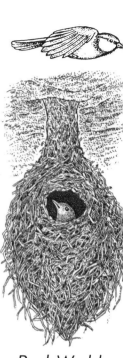

Song Thrushes

The male Thrush feeds the female. She sits on the eggs for two weeks.

Baby birds that hatch in nests are naked and blind. Their parents look after them.

Rock Warbler nest

Golden Oriole eggs

Hummingbird eggs

Kingfisher nest

113

Growing up

Song Thrush

Thrushes collect food from their home area near the nest.

Baby Thrushes stay in the nest for two weeks until most of their feathers have grown.

Baby birds are always hungry. When their parents land on the nest, the baby birds open their beaks wide and call loudly. The bright colours inside their beaks make their parents feed them.

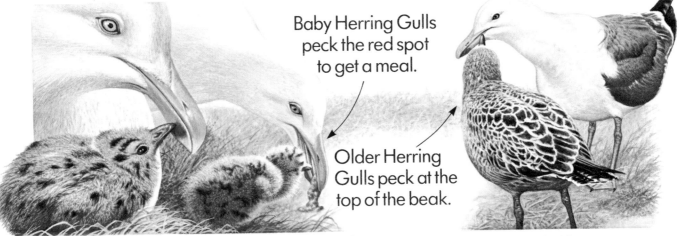

Baby Herring Gulls peck the red spot to get a meal.

Older Herring Gulls peck at the top of the beak.

Herring Gulls may have to fly far away to collect food for their babies. They swallow the food that they collect. When they get back, they cough up the food for the babies to eat.

Greylag Geese

Baby geese may watch their parents to find out what to eat.

They may sit on their mother's back if they are cold or tired.

A short time after they hatch, baby geese can swim. They will go into the water to escape from enemies.

Young geese take about six weeks to grow all their feathers.
They can now fly, but they may practise twisting and turning in the air.
They may also practise taking off and landing.

Resting and preening

At night most birds find a safe place to rest. They do not like flying at night because they cannot see well in the dark.

Hundreds of Starlings often fly to the same place every evening. They all rest together for the night.

Some birds tuck their beaks under their wings when they sleep. They fluff out their feathers to keep themselves warm.

Sparrows

Lots of Wrens may sleep together to keep warm.

Birds don't fall out of trees when they sleep. This is because when they bend their legs, their toes lock on to the branch.

All birds clean and tidy up their feathers.
This is called preening. Most birds also spread oil
on their feathers to keep them in good condition.

Birds squeeze oil
out of a gland
just above the tail.

Herring Gulls

oil gland

Lovebirds

Some birds preen each other.

Song Thrush

Some birds have a bath.

Birds that do not fly

The Ostrich is the largest bird in the world. It is too heavy to fly and it has only small wing feathers. The Ostrich cannot fly away from enemies, but it can look after itself in other ways.

It is taller than a man. It can see enemies a long way away.

The beak of an Ostrich is strong enough to crack the skull of an enemy.

The Ostrich has long legs with strong muscles. It can run faster than its enemies.

On its big toe, it has a dangerous claw. It could kick an enemy to death.

big toe

Penguins do not fly with their wings. Do you know how they use them?

Penguins use their wings as flippers. They can swim very fast on top of the water or under the water.

Penguins use their wings to help them balance.

These Penguins are hunting for fish.

Penguins use their wings and their beaks when they quarrel.

Penguins can jump out of the sea.

Rockhopper Penguins

Picture puzzle

There are 13 birds hidden in this picture.
Can you find them all?

CREEPY CRAWLIES

There is a Ladybird in this picture of a Stag Beetle. Can you find 10 more Ladybirds like this one hidden on the next 22 pages? (The big one on page 133 doesn't count!)

Looking at insects and other small animals

This part of the book is about animals called invertebrates, which means "no backbone". They have no skeleton inside their body. Most of the different kinds of invertebrates are insects, but not all. On these pages, you can see the six groups of land invertebrates described in this part of the book.

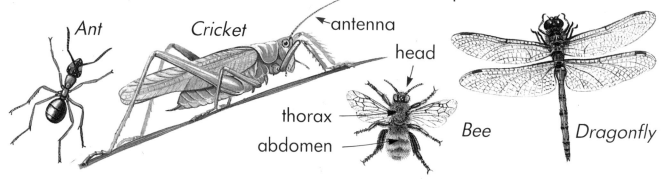

These are just four of the thousands of different kinds of insects. All adult insects have six legs and three parts to their body. They have a head, a middle section called the thorax, and an end section called the abdomen. On the head are two feelers called antennae. Most insects have wings at some stage in their lives.

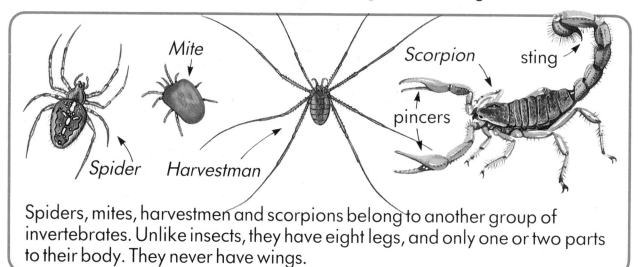

Spiders, mites, harvestmen and scorpions belong to another group of invertebrates. Unlike insects, they have eight legs, and only one or two parts to their body. They never have wings.

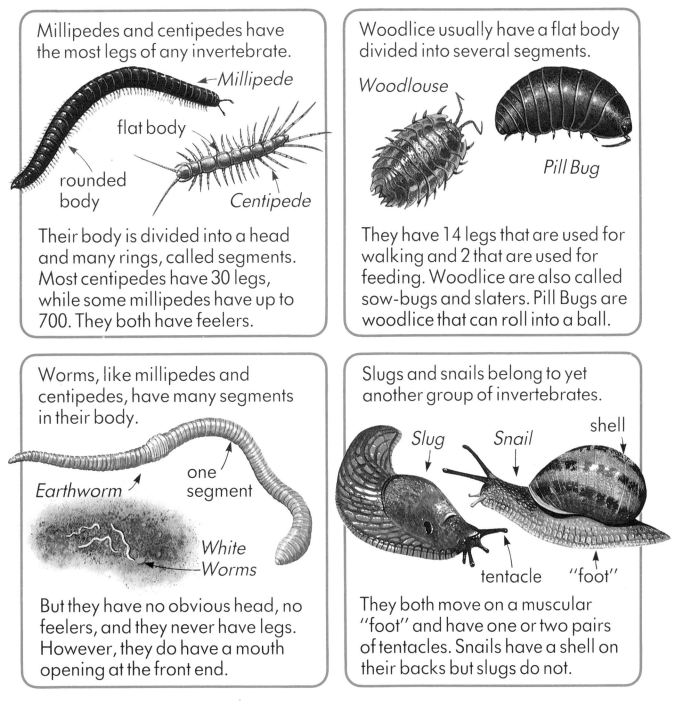

Millipedes and centipedes have the most legs of any invertebrate.

Millipede

flat body

rounded body

Centipede

Their body is divided into a head and many rings, called segments. Most centipedes have 30 legs, while some millipedes have up to 700. They both have feelers.

Woodlice usually have a flat body divided into several segments.

Woodlouse

Pill Bug

They have 14 legs that are used for walking and 2 that are used for feeding. Woodlice are also called sow-bugs and slaters. Pill Bugs are woodlice that can roll into a ball.

Worms, like millipedes and centipedes, have many segments in their body.

one segment

Earthworm

White Worms

But they have no obvious head, no feelers, and they never have legs. However, they do have a mouth opening at the front end.

Slugs and snails belong to yet another group of invertebrates.

shell

Slug   *Snail*

tentacle   "foot"

They both move on a muscular "foot" and have one or two pairs of tentacles. Snails have a shell on their backs but slugs do not.

123

How invertebrates move

Many insects can fly, using one or two pairs of wings. Some can fly very fast – a Dragonfly can do 40 kilometres an hour.

A beetle has two pairs of wings.

1. Hard wing cases.

2. Flight wings.

Beetles use one pair of wings in flight. They hold the wing cases out and move the flight wings up and down.

Bees use two pairs of wings in flight but it looks like one pair. Special hooks join the pairs of wings together.

hooks

flight wings

balancers

Flies have a second pair of tiny wings to help them balance.

How the wings move in flight

1

2

3

4

During the down stroke, the wings push the air downwards and backwards.

The up stroke of the wings.

Walking, jumping and crawling

This is a looper caterpillar. It brings its back legs up to the front legs and then moves the front legs forwards.

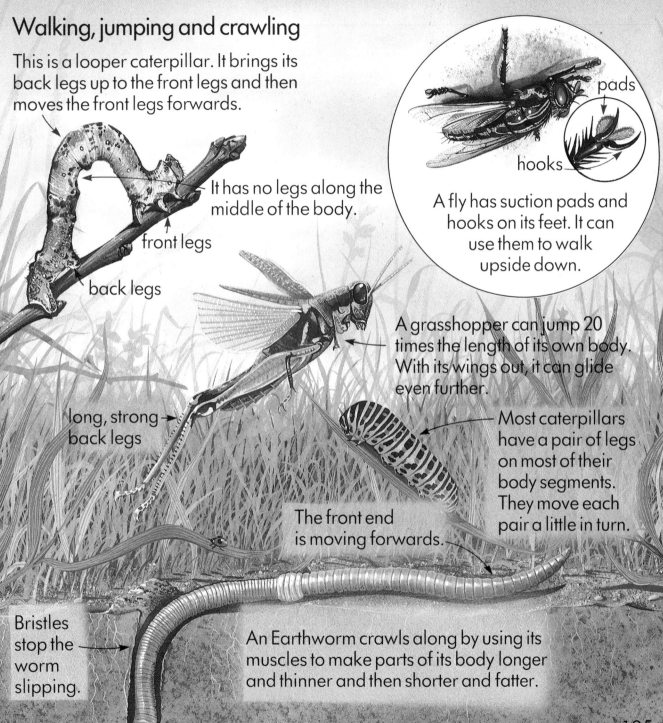

It has no legs along the middle of the body.

front legs

back legs

A fly has suction pads and hooks on its feet. It can use them to walk upside down.

pads

hooks

A grasshopper can jump 20 times the length of its own body. With its wings out, it can glide even further.

long, strong back legs

Most caterpillars have a pair of legs on most of their body segments. They move each pair a little in turn.

The front end is moving forwards.

Bristles stop the worm slipping.

An Earthworm crawls along by using its muscles to make parts of its body longer and thinner and then shorter and fatter.

125

How invertebrates feed

There are thousands of different invertebrates. They do not all find food or eat in the same way. Some eat plants, others eat animals or both animals and plants. A few invertebrates feed on blood.

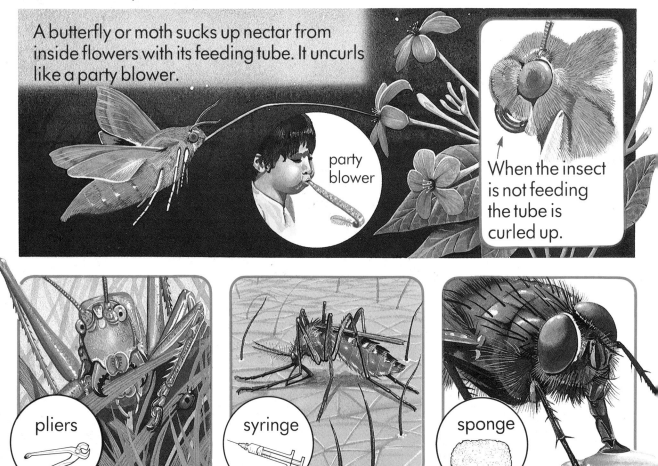

A butterfly or moth sucks up nectar from inside flowers with its feeding tube. It uncurls like a party blower.

party blower

When the insect is not feeding the tube is curled up.

pliers

A grasshopper's jaws work like a pair of pliers, nipping off bits of grass.

syringe

A female mosquito pierces the skin and sucks up blood, like a syringe.

sponge

The mouthparts of a fly soak up juices like a sponge mops up water.

Tarantula

eyes

All spiders
have eight
legs.

Poison from
the fangs
paralyses the
victim. Then the
spider sucks the
insides dry.

snake

These are not legs, but
special feelers called
palps. They are like the
antennae of insects.

This hairy Tarantula is a giant spider. It lives in
hot countries of America. It captures small
mammals, insects and small snakes.

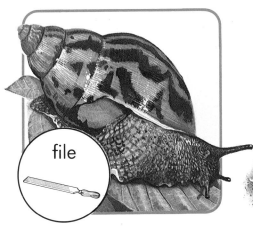

file

*Burying
Beetle*

This beetle is digging
soil from under the dead
bird, so it is slowly
buried.

A snail's tongue is like a
rough file. It feeds on
leaves, fruit and flowers.

Burying Beetles feed on dead animals they find. The
females also lay their eggs on the body once it is
buried. The young feed on the body when they hatch.

127

Colours and chemicals

Many invertebrates match the colour or the shape of their surroundings. They are camouflaged. If they keep still, they are difficult to see. Some invertebrates have bright colours to warn enemies not to touch. Others squirt harmful chemicals at their enemies.

The Peppered Moth is almost invisible on tree trunks.

The Thorn Bug looks like a thorn on a twig.

This Leaf Butterfly looks like a leaf when it is at rest.

This looper caterpillar looks like a twig.

big false eyes

abdomen

front legs

The Puss Moth caterpillar is camouflaged by its green body. It scares birds away by rearing its bright face and its tail.

The Flower Mantis looks like the flower on which it sits. Insects come to the flower to feed and get trapped by it.

Insects that are black and red, or yellow or black, usually taste nasty. Birds learn to leave them alone.

Cinnabar caterpillar

Cinnabar Moth

This Wood Ant is ready for battle. In this position it can squirt acid at enemies that come too near.

acid

If it is startled, the Bombardier Beetle fires a gas from its rear end that irritates the eyes of the enemy. The gas pops and also forms a smoke-screen. The beetle escapes while the enemy is confused. This drives off most enemies from ants, spiders and beetles to frogs and toads.

Leopard Frog

gas

Bombardier Beetle

Eggs and young

Most female invertebrates lay eggs. These are usually quite small. The eggs are laid alone or in groups, in different places. Usually each egg is put where there is food for the young when it hatches. You may be able to find some eggs if you look at leaves or grasses.

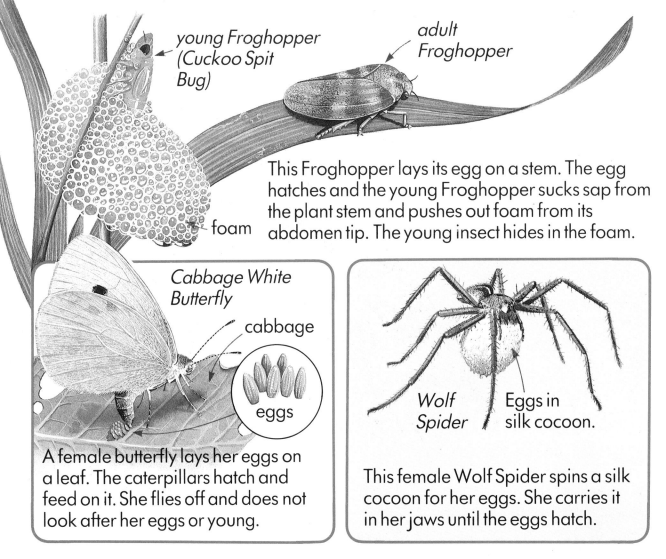

young Froghopper (Cuckoo Spit Bug)

adult Froghopper

foam

This Froghopper lays its egg on a stem. The egg hatches and the young Froghopper sucks sap from the plant stem and pushes out foam from its abdomen tip. The young insect hides in the foam.

Cabbage White Butterfly

cabbage

eggs

A female butterfly lays her eggs on a leaf. The caterpillars hatch and feed on it. She flies off and does not look after her eggs or young.

Wolf Spider

Eggs in silk cocoon.

This female Wolf Spider spins a silk cocoon for her eggs. She carries it in her jaws until the eggs hatch.

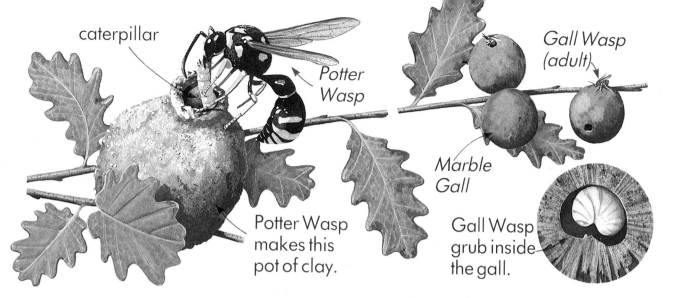

caterpillar

Potter Wasp

Potter Wasp makes this pot of clay.

Gall Wasp (adult)

Marble Gall

Gall Wasp grub inside the gall.

The Potter Wasp catches and paralyzes caterpillars. Then she pushes them into her clay pot. When it is full, she lays an egg inside. When the wasp grub hatches, it feeds on the caterpillars.

A Marble Gall is caused by a wasp that lays its egg in the bud of an oak. The oak swells around the grub and forms a gall. The wasp grub feeds on the gall until it changes into an adult wasp.

Garden Snail

eggs

A snail lays lots of eggs in the soil, then leaves them to hatch by themselves. The young look like very tiny snails.

Centipede

poison fang

Some female centipedes coil round their eggs in the soil and guard them fiercely. They will stab intruders with their poison fangs.

Growing up

When a young invertebrate hatches, it often looks different from its parents. The young changes its appearance at least once before it becomes an adult. Some young invertebrates look like their parents when they are born or when they hatch.

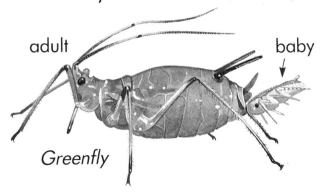

adult   baby

Greenfly

1. Eggs   2. Young

Some Greenfly do not lay eggs at all. They can give birth to babies without mating. The babies are tiny versions of the mother.

Female snails lay eggs. When the young hatch out, they look like very tiny adults. Their shells grow as the snails get bigger.

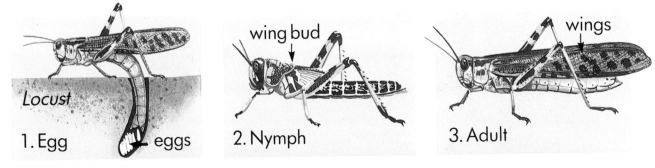

Locust

1. Egg   eggs

wing bud

2. Nymph

wings

3. Adult

A female locust lays her eggs in damp, warm soil and leaves them to hatch.

The young looks like an adult locust but has no wings, only wing buds.

The nymph grows and changes into an adult. The adult has wings.

1. Eggs

After mating, a Ladybird lays her eggs on a leaf.

eggs

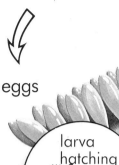

larva hatching

2. Larva

A larva hatches out of each egg. The larva eats a lot and grows fast.

adult Ladybird

larva

4. Adult

The pupa's skin splits and the adult Ladybird crawls out. The adult finds a mate.

pupa

3. Pupa

The larva changes into a pupa after two to five weeks. An adult Ladybird forms inside the pupa's skin.

How an invertebrate grows

The skin of some invertebrates will not stretch. So that it can grow, the animal forms a new larger skin under its old skin. When this is ready, it splits open the old skin near the head and wriggles out.

The animal, with its new skin, comes out forwards.

Centipede

head

The old skin is left behind.

133

Spiders

Spiders live in many different places. Some live in our own homes and gardens. Others live on mountains or in deserts. Most of the 60,000 different kinds of spiders are very useful to us. They eat lots of flies and other pests. All spiders have eight legs and can spin silk.

Silk is made by special organs in the abdomen.

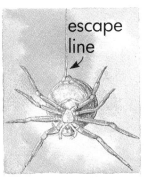

escape line

This spider spins a silk thread as an escape line.

This spider wraps its prey in silken threads.

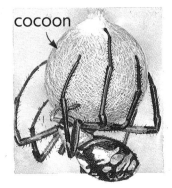

cocoon

Spiders spin a silk cocoon to protect their eggs.

web

An Orb Spider waits for its prey to become trapped in its web. The spider does not get stuck on its own web because it has oil on its feet.

This tiny Crab Spider looks like the flower it sits on. It waits in ambush for passing insects such as bees, then grabs one in its fangs.

The deadly ones

All spiders have sharp fangs with poison to paralyze or kill their prey. A few spiders are dangerous and can hurt people. Here are three of them.

The Red Back of Australia is called the Night Stinger in New Zealand.

Black Widow

In the United States, the female's poison is stronger than elsewhere. It can kill people.

This Funnelweb Spider lives around Sydney in Australia.

The Web-throwing Spider spins a net of sticky silk threads. It waits for its prey to walk under it. Then it throws the net over the prey.

The Trapdoor Spider waits in its tube until its prey is close. Then it strikes and drags the insect down into its silk-lined tunnel. The trapdoor shuts tight and the prey is killed.

trapdoor

net

Grasshopper (prey)

135

Slugs and snails

Slugs and snails belong to the group called gastropods. This means "bellyfoots". Slugs are land snails that have no shell.

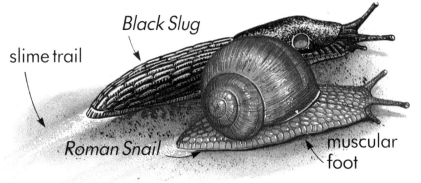

slime trail

Black Slug

Roman Snail

muscular foot

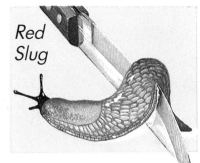

Red Slug

Slugs and snails make a slimy substance that helps them move along. They leave a slime trail. The flat underpart of their body is called a muscular foot.

A slug's slime is so protective that it can climb over a very sharp knife unharmed.

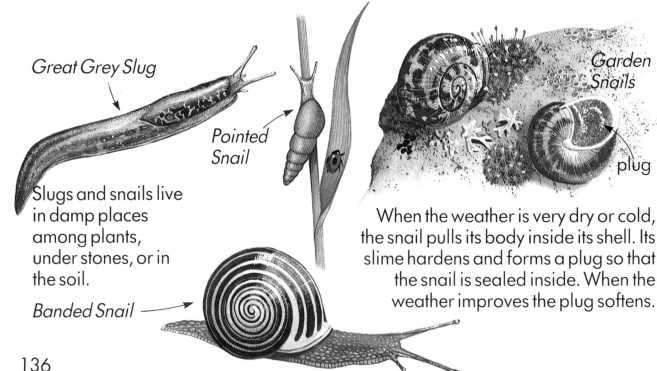

Great Grey Slug

Pointed Snail

Garden Snails

plug

Slugs and snails live in damp places among plants, under stones, or in the soil.

Banded Snail

When the weather is very dry or cold, the snail pulls its body inside its shell. Its slime hardens and forms a plug so that the snail is sealed inside. When the weather improves the plug softens.

There are Giant Snails in many parts of the world. This one comes from West Africa. One of the largest snails ever found measured 34 centimetres from the top of its shell to the tip of its head. Giant Snails eat all kinds of plants and their fruits, including bananas. They also eat dead animals.

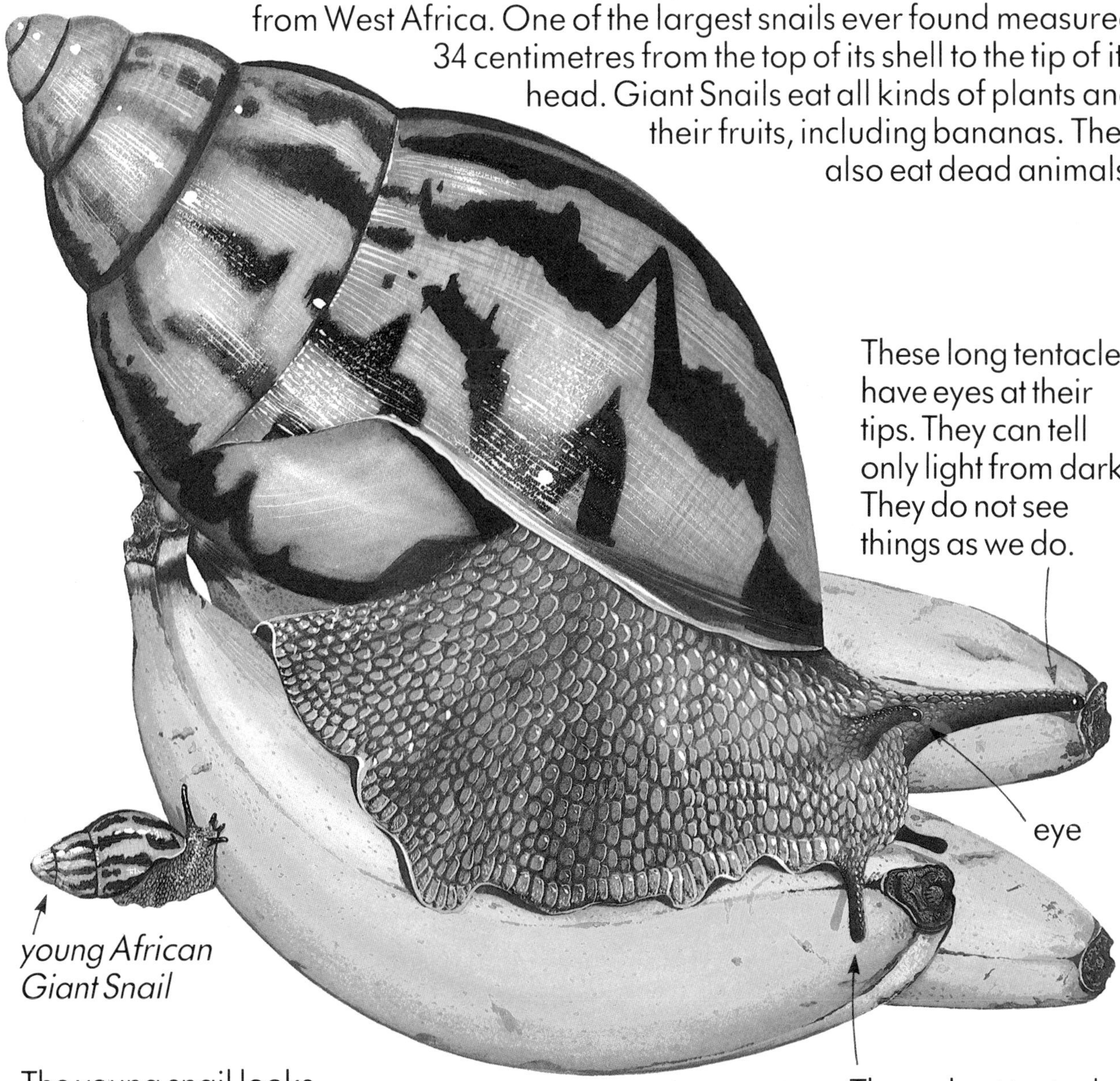

These long tentacles have eyes at their tips. They can tell only light from dark. They do not see things as we do.

eye

young African Giant Snail

The young snail looks just like its parent.

These short tentacles smell and feel things. They have no eyes.

Beetles

There are over 250,000 different kinds of beetles. Turn over a log in a forest or disturb some fallen leaves. You are likely to find a beetle.

Most beetles are quite small. A few grow to the size of these two beetles. They are drawn life size.

actual size

Flea Beetle
This is one of the smallest beetles in the world.

African Goliath Beetle
The heaviest beetle in the world is one like this. It weighs 100 grams.

American Hercules Beetle
The longest beetle in the world is one like this. It is 19 centimetres long.

Helpful beetles

This beetle was brought into America from its home in Australia. It eats the scale insect pests that damage orange and lemon trees in California.

Scale insect

Australian Cardinal Beetle

orange

Colorado Beetle

adult

Harmful beetles

Colorado Beetles and their larvae eat the leaves of potato plants. Their home is in the United States but they have travelled to most places where potatoes are grown. They can destroy a whole potato crop.

Living lanterns

←Fireflies and Glow-worms→ are not flies or worms. They are beetles. Both insects can produce light at the tip of their bodies. They use light to attract a mate. In hot countries you can see trees lit up by fireflies flashing.

Termite cities

Some insects live and work together in large family groups. They are called social insects. Termites, ants, and some bees and wasps are social insects. Some termites build huge mounds or nests. Most termites live in hot countries and feed on wood.

Jungle termite nests

A new roof is added each year.

Termite nest cut in half to show passages inside.

There are thousands of termites in each nest. These are workers and soldiers.

worker   soldier

In tropical rain forests, where it rains a lot, termites build their nests with a roof. This works like an umbrella. It keeps heavy rain from damaging the nest.

Tree termite nest

In tropical America some termites build their nests in trees. This Tree Ant-eater is eating the termites. It has a long, sticky tongue.

The queen lays eggs. The king fertilizes them.

Some African termite nests are built higher than a giraffe. A record one reached 12.8 metres in height. This is over twice the height of a giraffe.

African termite nest

In northern Australia the Compass Termites build nests with flattened sides. They have two narrow sides and two broad sides. The broad sides always face east and west. They catch the sun's rays at sunrise and sunset, when the rays are not too strong. At mid-day the rays are strong, but shine on the narrow sides, so the termites do not get too hot.

Compass termite nests

Workers care for the king and queen in a special chamber. The queen's body is swollen with eggs.

workers

queen

workers

king

Soldier termites guard the nest.

North

East

West

South

141

Amazing creepy crawlies

The longest earthworms live in Africa and Australia. They can grow to four times the length of this one.

Actual size of flea.

A flea can jump 200 times the length of its body. From here it would land on the head of the stick insect.

male Cicada

This is the loudest insect in the world. It can be heard from 400 metres.

Earthworms have tiny bristles on each segment. These grip the soil as the worm moves about.

The longest insect in the world is a stick insect. This Giant Stick Insect lives in Asia. It can grow as big as the one shown here.

How long is this stick insect? Measure it from its head to the tip of its abdomen. One stick insect grew to 33 centimetres.

opening on leg

A cricket hears with its "knees", where it has special openings.

Luna Moth
Moths can smell with their antennae.

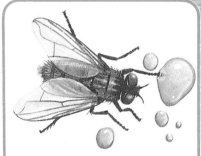

A fly tastes with its feet. It likes sweet foods, such as sugar.

Picture puzzle

All the invertebrates shown below have one or more things wrong with their bodies. Can you see what is wrong with each one? You can find them all in this part of the book. The answers are at the bottom of the page.

Answers: 1. Fly should have only one pair of wings. 2. Grasshopper's back legs should be larger. 3. Caterpillar shouldn't have legs on each segment. 4. Spider should have 8 legs. 5. Scorpion's sting and pincers are in wrong positions. 6. Ladybird should have 6 legs. 7. Beetle shouldn't have feathery antennae. 8. Snail should have two pairs of tentacles and its mouth and eyes are in the wrong place. 9. Earthworm should have no legs, no eyes and no tongue.

BUTTERFLIES
AND MOTHS

Games

2. Watch the butterfly move

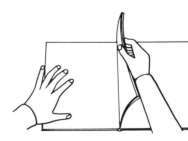

Hold the Butterfly pages like this.

1. Hunt the little green caterpillar

Can you find 11 caterpillars like this in the Butterfly pages?

Watch the top right hand corner and flick the pages over fast.

watch here

Looking at butterflies and moths

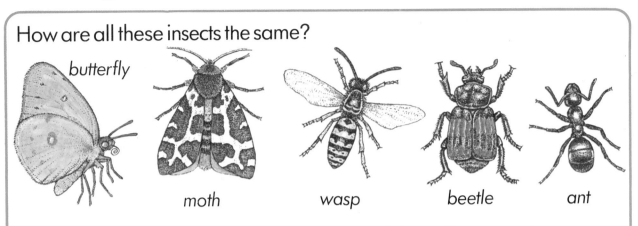

How are all these insects the same?

butterfly

moth

wasp

beetle

ant

Their bodies are made up of three parts and they all have six legs.

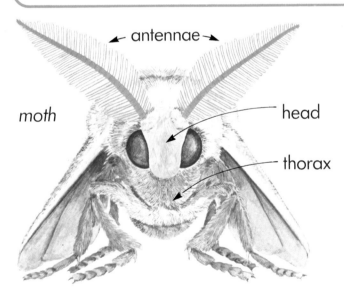

antennae

moth

head

thorax

Butterflies and moths have hooks on their feet for holding on tight. They feel and smell with their long antennae.

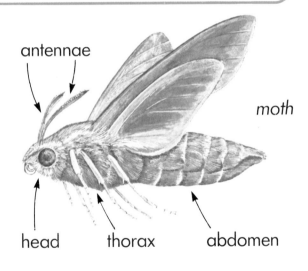

antennae

moth

head

thorax

abdomen

Behind the head is the thorax. The wings join on to the thorax. The long part of the body is called the abdomen.

Some insects have four wings, some have two wings and some have no wings. How many wings have butterflies and moths got?

The wings are not joined together, but they move together when the butterfly flies.

Swallowtail Butterfly

The front wings do most of the work. If they are damaged, the butterfly may not be able to fly properly.

If the back wings are damaged, the butterfly can still fly.

Butterflies and moths have four wings.

Looking at wings

*Red
Underwing
Moth*

*Oleander
Hawk Moth*

*Walnut
Moth*

When butterflies rest,
they usually close their
wings above their backs.

*Common
Blue Butterfly*

The wings of a butterfly or
moth are often one colour
on the outside and a different
colour on the inside.

When moths rest, they fold
their wings over their backs,
or spread them out flat.

*Privet
Hawk Moth*

When butterflies and moths
rest, the colour of the outside
of their wings makes it hard
for enemies to see them.

*Lappet
Moth*

*Scallop Shell
Moth*

*Small
Skipper
Butterfly*

Buff-tip Moth

Some butterflies look like dead leaves when they rest. They are hard to see.

Some moths look like twigs when they rest. It is hard for enemies to see them.

What makes the colours on their wings?

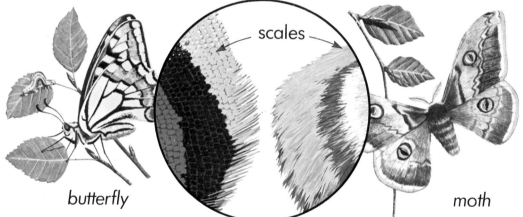

scales

butterfly

moth

Brimstone Butterfly

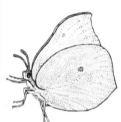

Red Admiral Butterfly

The wings are covered with coloured or shiny scales. If you touch the wings the scales will rub off.

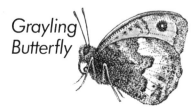

Grayling Butterfly

Green Hairstreak Butterfly

Monarch Butterfly

149

Keeping warm and feeding

Butterflies and moths need to be warm for their bodies to work properly. When the air is cold, they rest.

Butterflies warm up in the sun.

Titania's Fritillary

The dark parts of the wings warm up quickly. Butterflies from cold countries often have dark colours on their wings.

Flannel Moth

Moths are often very hairy. The hairs on their bodies help to keep them warm at night.

Elephant Hawk Moth

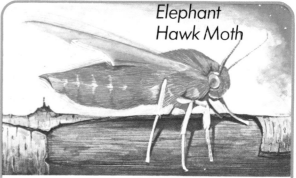

Moths often shiver before they fly. The shivering helps to warm up their bodies.

Butterflies and moths do not eat to grow larger.
They use food to make heat inside their bodies.
Heat makes energy. This keeps their bodies working.

*Hummingbird
Hawk Moth*

Moths and butterflies drink
a sweet liquid from flowers.
This liquid is called nectar.

They drink nectar through
a long tube called
a proboscis.

proboscis

*Union Jack
Butterfly*

Some butterflies
can taste
with their feet.

*Lime
Hawk Moth*

sap

Moths may drink sap from
trees or damaged plants.

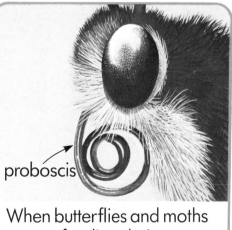

proboscis

When butterflies and moths
are not feeding, their
proboscis is curled up.

A butterfly's day

Common Blue Butterfly

1. The butterfly rests at night when it is cold.

2. When the sun comes out, she warms up.

3. She looks for a place to lay her eggs.

4. She lays her eggs on a special plant.

A moth's night

Privet Hawk Moth

male

1. The moth hides in the day.

2. At dusk he shivers to warm himself up.

3. He flies away to find a female.

4. He drinks some nectar from a flower.

5. She warms up again in the sun.

6. Now she is warm enough to fly away.

7. She lands on a flower to drink nectar.

8. When it gets dark and cold, she hides.

5. Now it is very cold so he rests.

6. When it gets warmer, he flies away.

7. He finds a female and mates with her.

8. When it gets light, he hides.

153

Finding a partner

The most important thing that a butterfly or moth has to do is to find a partner for mating. When a female has mated she will lay her eggs.

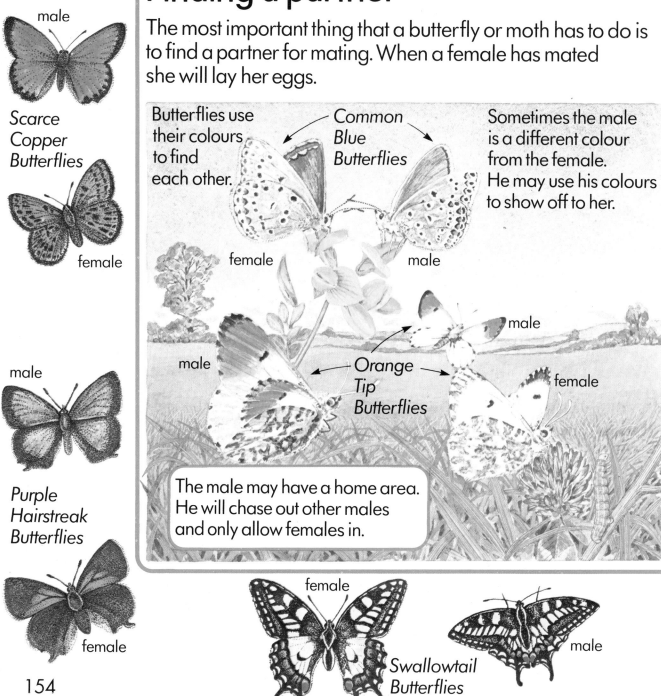

male

Scarce Copper Butterflies

female

male

Purple Hairstreak Butterflies

female

Butterflies use their colours to find each other.

Common Blue Butterflies

female

male

Sometimes the male is a different colour from the female. He may use his colours to show off to her.

male

male

Orange Tip Butterflies

female

The male may have a home area. He will chase out other males and only allow females in.

female

Swallowtail Butterflies

male

154

You can often tell a male moth from a female moth by his larger antennae.

female

Emperor Moths

male

At night, moths cannot use colour to find each other.
Instead the male finds the female by her scent.
Each kind of moth has a different scent.

The female gives off a special scent to attract a male.

Gypsy Moths

The male uses his feathery antennae as scent nets. He can smell a female from far away.

male

Muslin Moths

female

male

Hag Moths

female

Oak Eggar Moths

male

female

155

Mating and laying eggs

A pair of butterflies may play together before they mate.
This is called courtship.

The male is holding
the antennae
of the female
between
his wings.

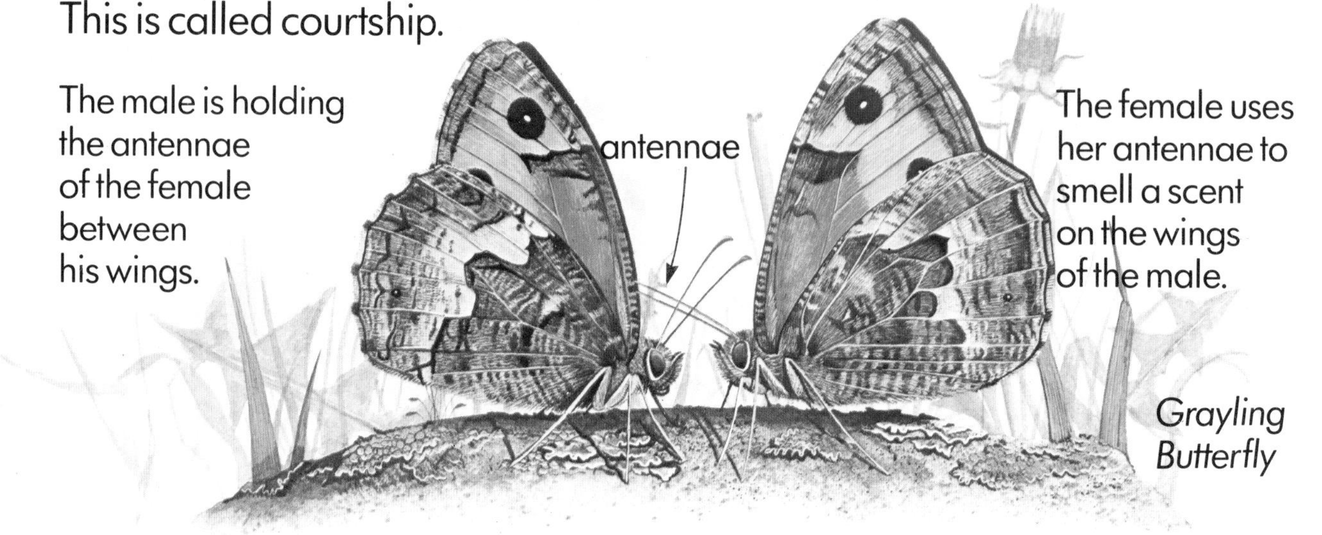

antennae

The female uses
her antennae to
smell a scent
on the wings
of the male.

*Grayling
Butterfly*

When butterflies or moths mate, they join their abdomens together.
A bag of sperm passes from the male to the female.
The sperm joins with eggs inside the female.

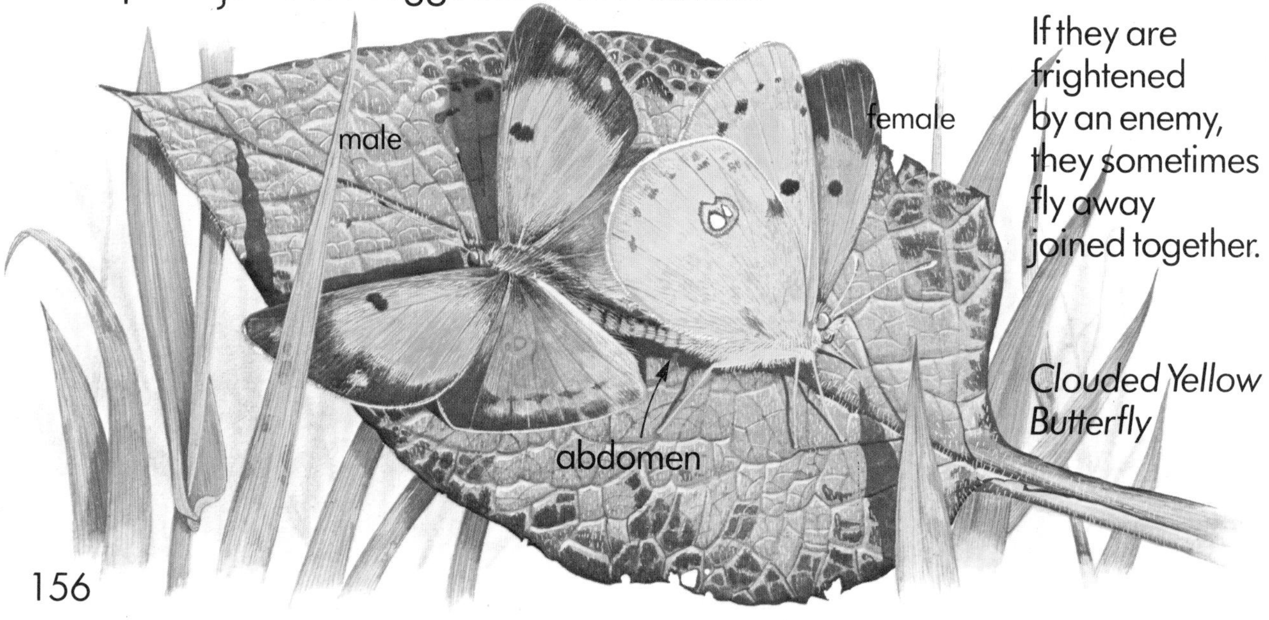

male

female

If they are
frightened
by an enemy,
they sometimes
fly away
joined together.

*Clouded Yellow
Butterfly*

abdomen

A female may have hundreds of eggs inside her. She will lay her eggs when she has mated.

Nettle leaf

eggs

Map Butterfly

A butterfly or moth usually lays her eggs on a special plant. She can lay lots of eggs together, or one egg at a time.

Bulrush Wainscot Moth

abdomen

This moth lays each egg inside a Bulrush. She makes holes in the stem with spines on the end of her abdomen.

Lackey Moth

This Moth sticks her eggs round a twig.

egg

Leopard Moth

This Moth sticks her eggs on to tree bark.

egg

Marbled White Butterfly

This Butterfly lays her eggs as she flies.

egg

157

The hungry caterpillar

Out of each egg comes a caterpillar. It eats and eats, and grows and grows. When it is big enough to start changing into an adult butterfly or moth, it stops growing.

1. A moth caterpillar is inside this egg.

2. The caterpillar eats a hole in the egg and crawls out.

3. It is very hungry, so it eats the old egg shell.

old skin

4. It eats the top of the leaf. Soon the caterpillar grows too big for its skin.

5. The skin splits and the caterpillar wriggles out. It is wearing a new skin.

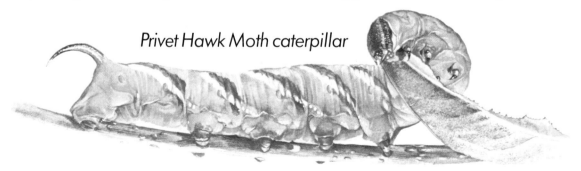

Privet Hawk Moth caterpillar

6. The caterpillar eats Privet leaves. It eats and grows and eats and grows. It changes its skin three more times.

The caterpillar cannot see very well. It has twelve tiny eyes on its head. The eyes are too small for you to see.

Mouth parts for chewing.

The three pairs of front legs hold on to the food.

The five pairs of fleshy legs are called claspers. They can grip tightly to a stalk.

The caterpillar breathes through air holes in the side of its body. There is an air hole in the centre of each coloured spot.

Caterpillars and pupae

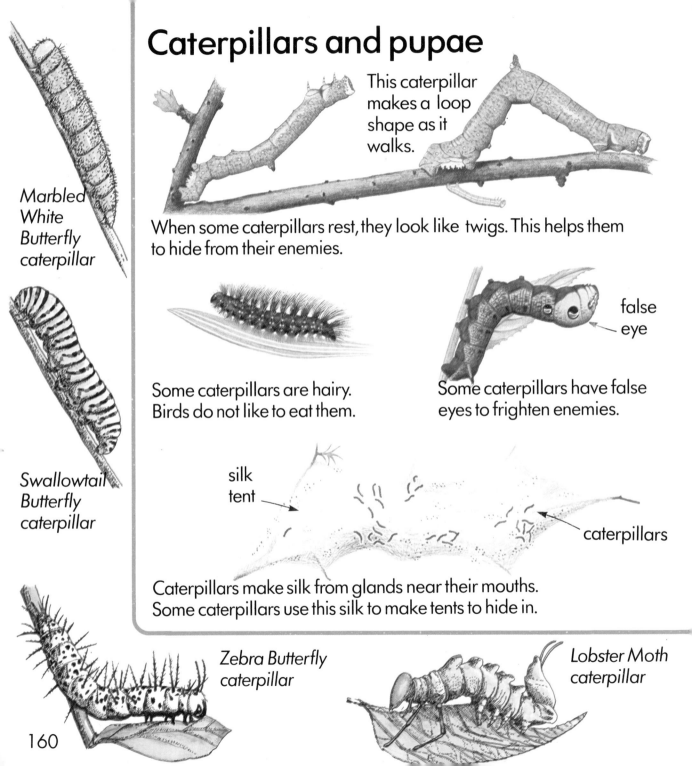

This caterpillar makes a loop shape as it walks.

When some caterpillars rest, they look like twigs. This helps them to hide from their enemies.

Marbled White Butterfly caterpillar

false eye

Some caterpillars are hairy. Birds do not like to eat them.

Some caterpillars have false eyes to frighten enemies.

Swallowtail Butterfly caterpillar

silk tent

caterpillars

Caterpillars make silk from glands near their mouths. Some caterpillars use this silk to make tents to hide in.

Zebra Butterfly caterpillar

Lobster Moth caterpillar

When caterpillars are fully grown, they change into pupae.

Peacock Butterfly caterpillar

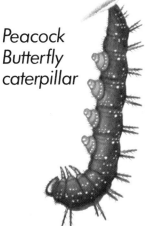

old skin

pupa

1. When this caterpillar is fully grown, it hangs upside down.

2. The caterpillar changes into a pupa inside its skin.

3. When the pupa wriggles, the skin splits. and slides up the pupa.

Cabbage White Butterfly pupa

4. The pupa skin is now hard. It has changed colour.

Some moth caterpillars bury themselves in the ground. Then they change into pupae.

silk cocoon

Some moth caterpillars spin silk cocoons around themselves. The caterpillars change into pupae inside the cocoons.

Bagworm Moth cocoon

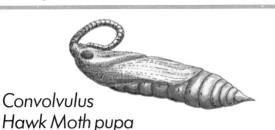

Convolvulus Hawk Moth pupa

Orange Tip Butterfly pupa

161

The magic change

Inside a pupa, a butterfly or moth is being made.

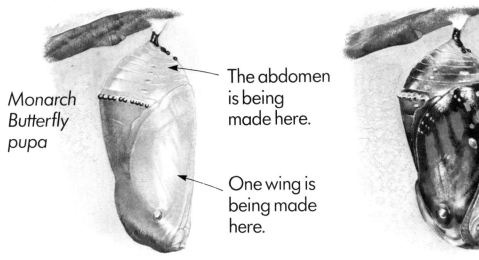

Monarch Butterfly pupa

The abdomen is being made here.

One wing is being made here.

One antenna is being made here.

One eye is being made here.

1. This pupa is two days old. A Monarch Butterfly is being made inside it.

2. The pupa is now two weeks old. The Butterfly is nearly ready to come out.

The Butterfly is pulling out its antennae, legs and proboscis.

3. The pupa skin splits. The head and legs of the Butterfly come out first.

At first,
the wings
are crumpled.

veins

The proboscis
is in
two parts.

4. The Butterfly pulls out its abdomen. It pumps blood into the veins of its wings.

5. Blood is pumping from the abdomen into the veins. This makes the wings unfold.

6. The Butterfly waits for its wings to dry and become stiff. Then it will be able to fly away.

The two parts of the proboscis join together to make a tube.

How long do they live?

A butterfly or moth goes through four stages in its life. Adult butterflies and moths usually live only a few days or weeks. When they have mated and the female has laid her eggs, the adults die.

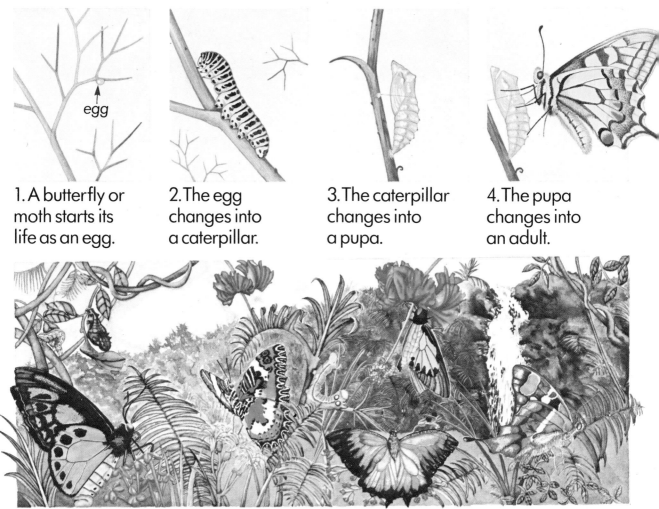

1. A butterfly or moth starts its life as an egg.

2. The egg changes into a caterpillar.

3. The caterpillar changes into a pupa.

4. The pupa changes into an adult.

In tropical countries, where the weather is always hot, a butterfly or moth often takes only a few weeks to change from an egg into an adult.

In colder countries, a butterfly or moth may take several months to change from an egg to an adult. In countries with very cold winters, they go into a deep sleep. They wake up when the weather gets warmer.

The Lackey Moth spends the winter as an egg.

The Herald Moth sleeps through the winter as an adult.

The Cabbage White Butterfly spends the winter as a pupa.

The Privet Hawk Moth spends the winter as a pupa in the soil.

The Marbled White Butterfly sleeps through the winter as a young caterpillar.

Butterflies and moths that spend part of their lives sleeping through the winter may take a year to change from an egg to an adult.

Enemies

Butterflies and moths have lots of enemies.

Birds eat them.

Spiders eat them.

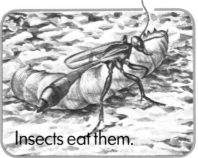
Insects eat them.

At night, many moths are eaten by bats.

Some moths have ears on the sides of their bodies. They help them to hear the squeaks that bats make. If these moths hear a bat coming, they drop to the ground or try to dodge out of the way.

Blue Underwing Moth

Some butterflies and moths have special colours. They use them to frighten away enemies.

Red Underwing Moth

If an enemy disturbs this moth, it opens and closes its wings. The flash of red may frighten away the enemy.

Owl Butterfly

This butterfly has false eyes on its wings. Birds may think they are the eyes of a dangerous animal.

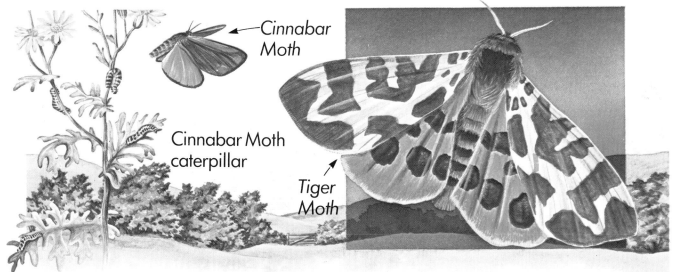

Cinnabar Moth

Cinnabar Moth caterpillar

Tiger Moth

Most butterflies and moths that are red and black, or yellow and black, taste nasty. Birds learn to leave them alone.

At night, Tiger Moths make clicking noises. Bats soon learn that moths that make this noise taste bad.

167

Picture puzzle

There are four butterflies, three moths and four caterpillars hidden in this picture. How many can you find?

FISHES

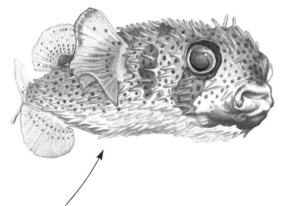

Porcupine Fishes normally
look like this.

When they are frightened, they
can blow themselves up with
water like this. Then other
fishes are less likely to eat them.

What is a fish?

Fishes are animals that live in water. They breathe through gills and have a skeleton inside the body. Their bodies usually stay at the same temperature as the water around them. Most fishes lay eggs.

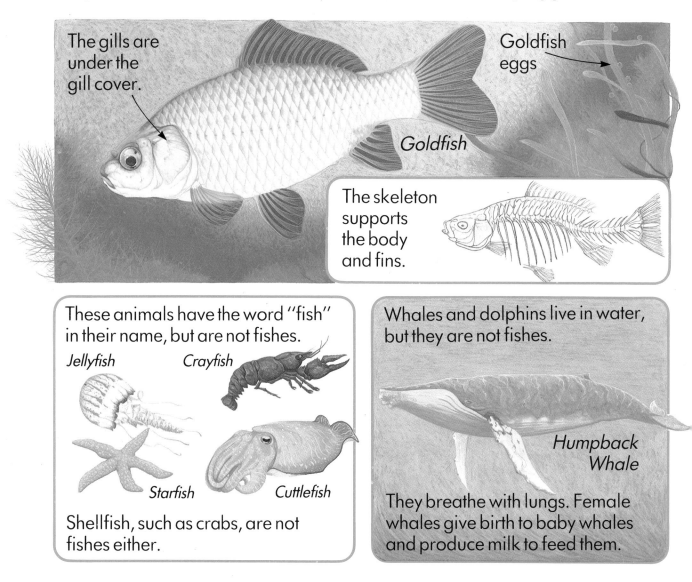

The gills are under the gill cover.

Goldfish eggs

Goldfish

The skeleton supports the body and fins.

These animals have the word "fish" in their name, but are not fishes.

Jellyfish

Crayfish

Starfish

Cuttlefish

Shellfish, such as crabs, are not fishes either.

Whales and dolphins live in water, but they are not fishes.

Humpback Whale

They breathe with lungs. Female whales give birth to baby whales and produce milk to feed them.

There are three main kinds of fishes.

1. Bony fishes

Most fishes have a skeleton made of bone. Their bodies are usually covered by very thin scales.

Bony fishes have a gill cover.

Thin, overlapping scales.

Perch

2. Sharks and Rays

scales

Skate (a type of ray)

These openings lead to the gills.

Blue Shark

Gill openings

scales

Sharks and rays have a skeleton made of gristle. Gristle is softer than bone, and can bend a little, but is still very tough. Sharks and rays are covered with lots of tiny scales. The scales are half buried in the skin.

3. Lampreys

Gill openings

Sucker disc (used for feeding)

Smooth skin with no scales.

River Lamprey (about 30 centimetres long)

Lampreys have no jaws and no scales. The skeleton is made of gristle.

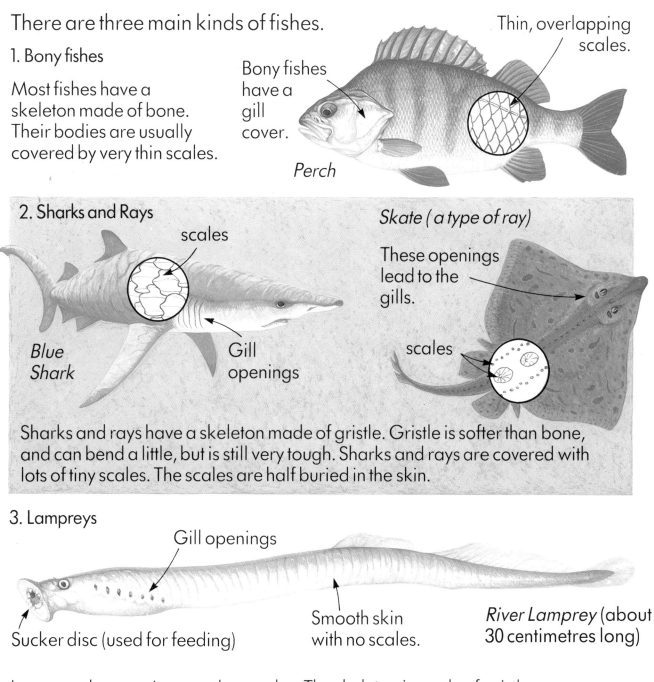

How fishes move

Most fishes swim using their fins. Some fins move the body forward. Others help to keep the fish the right way up.

The Bass's tail sweeps from side to side. This pushes the fish forward. The other fins keep the body steady.

The Manta Ray has huge side fins. They beat up and down like wings. The fish "flies" through the water.

The back fin of the Seahorse keeps moving in an S-shape. It drives the fish forwards.

The Eel's whole body wriggles to push the fish forward.

Eels usually have small fins.

Some fishes move in unusual ways.

*South American freshwater
Hatchet Fish*

Long
side
fin

Flying Fishes are chased
by dolphins and sharks.

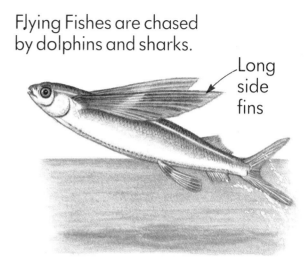

Long
side
fins

Some Hatchet Fishes can leap from the
water. They fly through the air by
beating their fins very fast. As they do
this, the fins make a buzzing sound.

Flying Fishes swim very fast under the
water using the tail fin. Suddenly they
burst through the surface and spread
out their fins. They glide in the air.

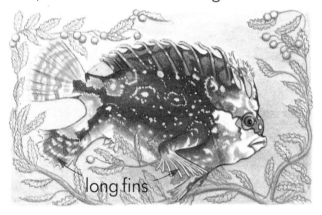

long fins

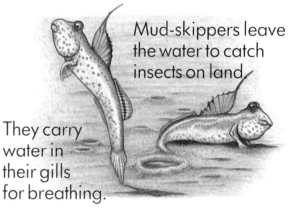

Mud-skippers leave
the water to catch
insects on land

They carry
water in
their gills
for breathing.

Frogfishes have fins at the ends of four
short "arms". They crawl about
amongst coral and seaweed looking
for food.

Mud-skippers can jump. They curl the
tail around against the mud. Suddenly
they jerk the body straight. The whole
fish jumps forwards.

How fishes breathe

Fishes need a gas called oxygen to live. There is oxygen in the water, and most fishes get it by using their gills. The blood inside the gills takes up oxygen from the water.

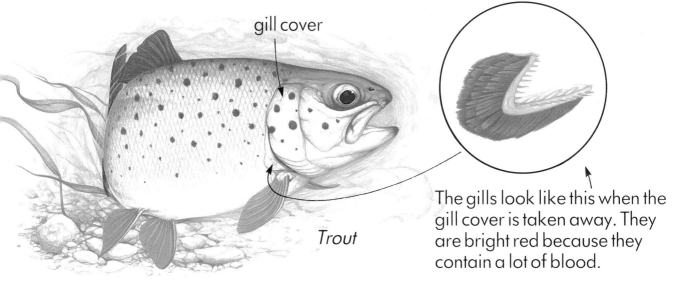

gill cover

Trout

The gills look like this when the gill cover is taken away. They are bright red because they contain a lot of blood.

The pictures below show how most fishes breathe.

Mouth open
WATER

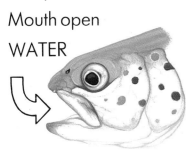

1. The fish gulps a big mouthful of water. Then it closes its mouth.

Mouth shut

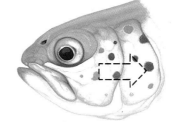

2. This pushes the water between the gills. The blood in the gills takes up the oxygen.

Mouth shut

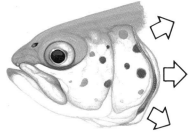

3. The blood carries oxygen around the body. The water comes out through the gill opening.

mouth

gill slits

Underside of
Thornback Ray.

Water enters
through holes.

eyes

Thornback Ray
resting
on the sand.

The mouth of a ray is on the underside of its body. When the ray rests on the sand, it cannot gulp a mouthful of clean water. Instead, it takes in water through two holes on top of its head. The water goes down over the gills and is pumped out through the gill slits.

Lungfishes have lungs as well as gills.

African Lungfishes usually live underwater in lakes. They use their gills and lungs to breathe. They gulp air at the surface of the water.

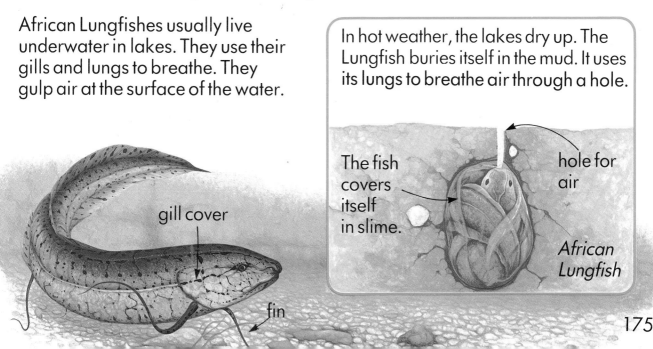

In hot weather, the lakes dry up. The Lungfish buries itself in the mud. It uses its lungs to breathe air through a hole.

The fish covers itself in slime.

hole for air

African Lungfish

gill cover

fin

How fishes find their way around

Like us, fishes can smell, see, taste, and hear. They also have special senses to help them find their way around.

Smelling

Most fishes have two pairs of nostrils.

Moray Eel

A fish has a good sense of smell. It uses its nostrils for smelling, but not for breathing.

Seeing

The eyes bulge out.

It can see the movement of things at the sides.

Sea Angelfish

Fishes can see very clearly in front of them, but not so clearly at the sides. Many fishes see in colour.

Tasting and feeling

Catfish

Some fishes have feelers on their chin and lips. The feelers are called barbels. The fish can taste with its barbels. It can also use them to search for food.

barbel

Hearing

Striped Drum Fish

Fishes have ears inside their heads. This fish lives in murky water, so hearing is more important to it than seeing. It finds other Drum Fish by making loud drumming noises.

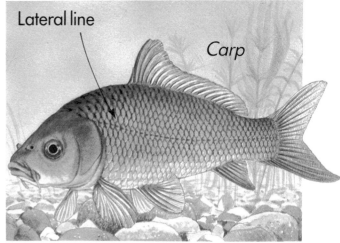

Lateral line

Carp

Most fishes have a line running along each side of their body. It is called the lateral line. The little holes in the line can sense the movements made by other animals in the water.

A few fishes have a special part of the body which makes electricity.

This Elephant Fish can electrify the water around it.

These lines show where the fish sends electricity.

As Elephant Fishes move around, they notice anything which alters this electricity. This stops them from bumping into things. It also helps them to find each other. They can easily swim backwards using this sense.

Ways of catching food

Fishes do not have regular meals. They eat what they can when they can. Some may go without food for days. Others catch food all the time. The shape of a fish's mouth often shows how it catches its food.

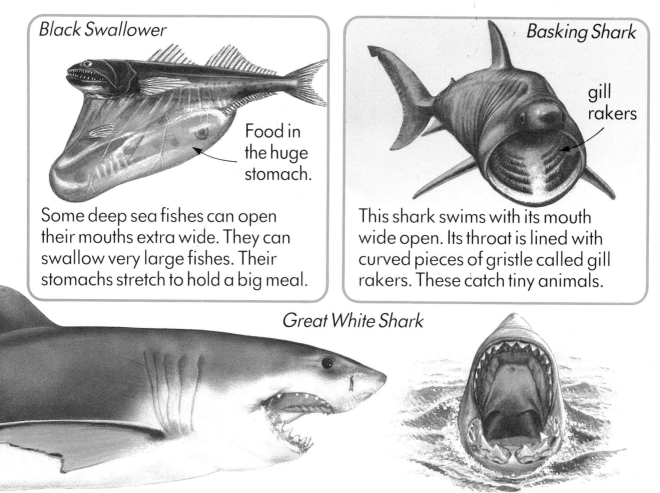

Black Swallower

Food in the huge stomach.

Some deep sea fishes can open their mouths extra wide. They can swallow very large fishes. Their stomachs stretch to hold a big meal.

Basking Shark

gill rakers

This shark swims with its mouth wide open. Its throat is lined with curved pieces of gristle called gill rakers. These catch tiny animals.

Great White Shark

The Great White Shark is big and strong. It can catch almost anything in the sea. Its teeth are sharp and triangular. As each tooth wears away or falls out, a new tooth from the row behind it takes its place.

Some fishes catch their food in cunning ways.

African freshwater Butterfly Fish

This fish lies in wait just under the surface of the water. When an insect lands, the fish leaps to grab it.

Malaysian Archer Fish

When the insect falls into the water, the fish eats it.

This fish can spit water at insects and spiders above the surface. The tiny jet of water knocks them off plants.

Angler Fish

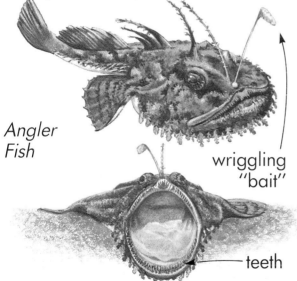

wriggling "bait"

teeth

Part of this fish's body forms a kind of "fishing rod" and "bait". Small fishes mistake the "bait" for food and come too close. They get caught and eaten.

American Garpike

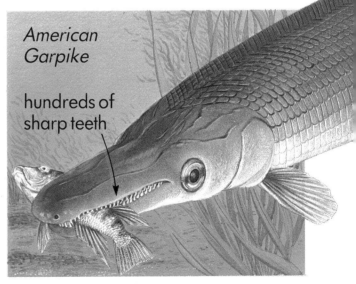

hundreds of sharp teeth

The Garpike lies quietly at the surface or in the weeds. When a fish comes near, it turns slowly to face its prey, then charges.

179

Colours in fishes

Many fishes are covered with brightly coloured patterns. In their natural surroundings, these markings help them to hide.

The Mackerel's colouring helps it to avoid its enemies, such as birds and big fishes. It is well camouflaged.

It has a dark blue pattern on its back.

Its belly and sides are white.

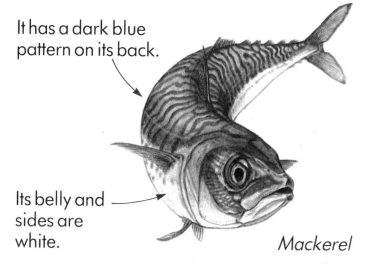

Mackerel

If you look down on a Mackerel from a boat, its blue back seems to merge with the water.

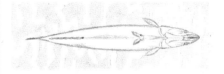

If you look up at a Mackerel from below, its white belly seems to merge with the sky.

Fishes like this Pike feed on other fishes. It lies in wait amongst the reeds. The blotches on its body blend with the reed stems, making it hard to see.

Many fishes living on the sea bed can change colour as they move about. The colour of this Australian Wobbegong (a shark) matches the sand and gravel.

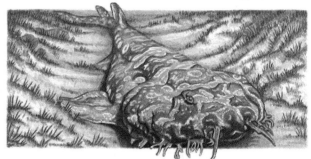

Some fishes use bright colours or bold markings to trick their enemies or to warn them to keep away.

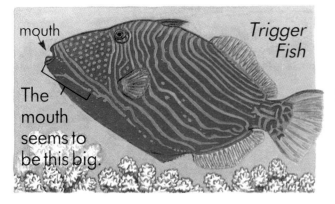

mouth

Trigger Fish

The mouth seems to be this big.

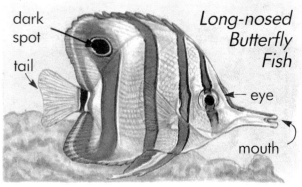

dark spot

tail

Long-nosed Butterfly Fish

eye

mouth

This Trigger Fish has dark markings on the lips and face. The mouth looks much bigger and fiercer than it really is. Other fishes keep away.

Many Butterfly Fishes have a dark spot near the tail. It looks like an eye. This confuses other fishes because the head seems to be where the tail is.

This fish has spines on its back and is brightly coloured. The spines have poison in them and the colours warn other fishes to keep away.

Lion Fish

Finding a mate and making a nest

Most fishes just come together in groups to lay their eggs. In some fishes, however, one male and one female form a pair. The male shows off to the female. This is called displaying.

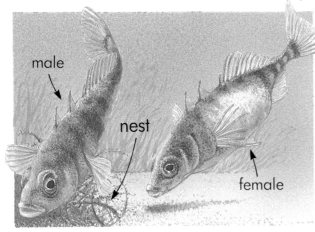

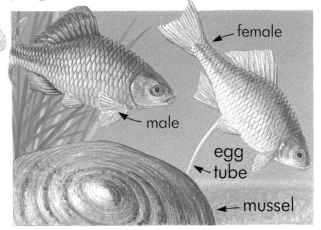

The male Stickleback displays his red belly to the female. This coaxes her to lay her eggs in the nest he has built. He drives other males away.

The male Bitterling displays to the female and leads her to a live mussel. She lays her eggs inside it through a special egg-laying tube.

The male Dragonet is brilliantly coloured. He has a very big pointed fin on his back. He keeps lifting it to attract a female.

Some fishes make a nest. Others just hide their eggs. But in both cases, the eggs are safe from being eaten or being washed away by the water.

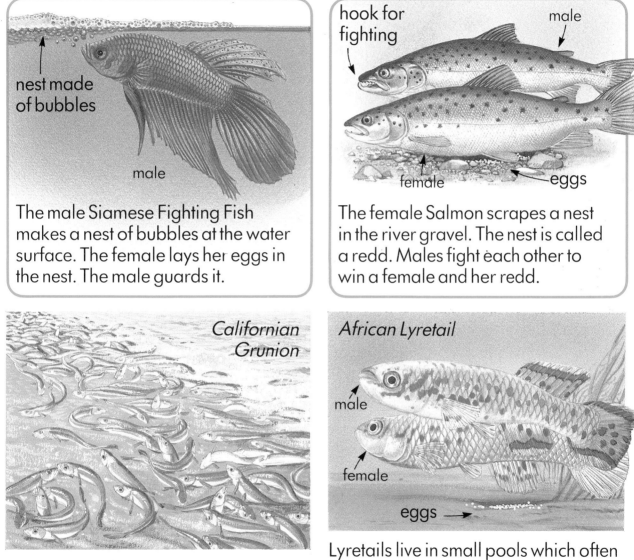

nest made of bubbles

male

The male Siamese Fighting Fish makes a nest of bubbles at the water surface. The female lays her eggs in the nest. The male guards it.

hook for fighting

male

female

eggs

The female Salmon scrapes a nest in the river gravel. The nest is called a redd. Males fight each other to win a female and her redd.

Californian Grunion

These fishes are brought on to the shore by the high tide. They bury their eggs in the sand on the beach.

African Lyretail

male

female

eggs

Lyretails live in small pools which often dry up. They bury their eggs in the mud. The baby fishes do not hatch until it rains again.

Fish eggs and babies

Most fishes lay lots of very small eggs. Some eggs float in the sea, and others stick to plants and rocks. The parents do not usually look after them.

eye

Trout egg

1. Fish eggs have a lot of yolk inside them. The baby grows by feeding on the yolk.

Fins beginning to grow.

yolk

newly-hatched Trout

2. The baby fish has hatched, but it still lives on the stored food in the yolk.

young Trout

3. The yolk lasts until the fins of the young fish are fully grown.

Remains of yolk.

Some fishes lay a few large eggs. Dogfish eggs are laid inside a case which becomes hard in the sea. The case protects the egg as it grows.

Dogfish

Egg case of Dogfish

Some bony fishes look after their eggs until the young hatch out.

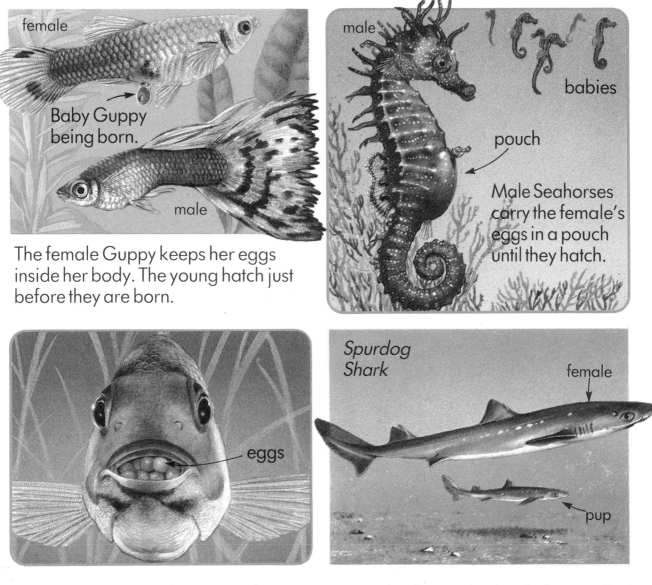

female

Baby Guppy being born.

male

male

babies

pouch

Male Seahorses carry the female's eggs in a pouch until they hatch.

The female Guppy keeps her eggs inside her body. The young hatch just before they are born.

eggs

Spurdog Shark

female

pup

Male Tilapias carry the eggs in their mouth. They also shelter the young fishes in their mouth.

Some sharks give birth to babies, called pups. Others lay eggs in a hard egg case and leave them to hatch out.

Life in fresh water

Many different kinds of fishes can live in the same river, because they like different parts of the river.

The Trout likes a fast-flowing mountain stream. The water is clean and cold. There is plenty of oxygen in the water.

The Minnow prefers streams which flow more slowly. The water has to be clean.

The Chub likes gently flowing rivers which are deep.

The Bream prefers rivers which flow very slowly.

The water in some streams and rivers flows very fast. The fishes must make sure that they are not swept away by the strong current.

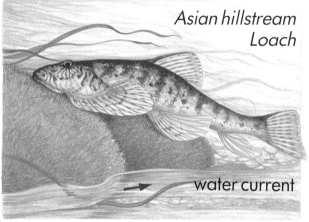

Some fishes, like this baby Salmon, hide behind stones to escape the current.

This fish is flat underneath. It can cling to big stones on the bed of the stream.

These fishes are well suited to the places where they live.

This Angelfish is very thin. It can swim between plant stems, and hide in them from its enemies.

This fish lives in freshwater lakes in caves. It has no eyes, but it can find its way around in the dark.

Life in the shallow seas

The shallow seas around the seashore have lots of food and hiding places for fishes. Many different kinds of fishes live there.

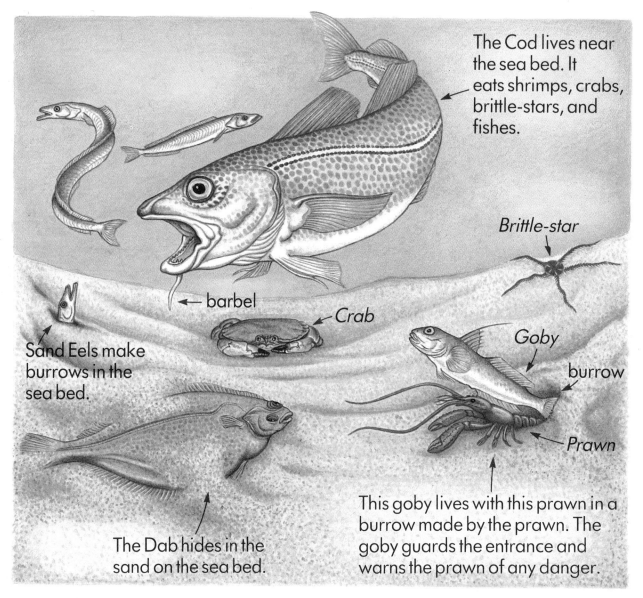

The Cod lives near the sea bed. It eats shrimps, crabs, brittle-stars, and fishes.

Brittle-star

← barbel

Crab

Goby

burrow

Prawn

Sand Eels make burrows in the sea bed.

The Dab hides in the sand on the sea bed.

This goby lives with this prawn in a burrow made by the prawn. The goby guards the entrance and warns the prawn of any danger.

A coral reef is the best place to find fishes. They can live or hide all over the reef. Some fishes eat coral, as well as sheltering in it.

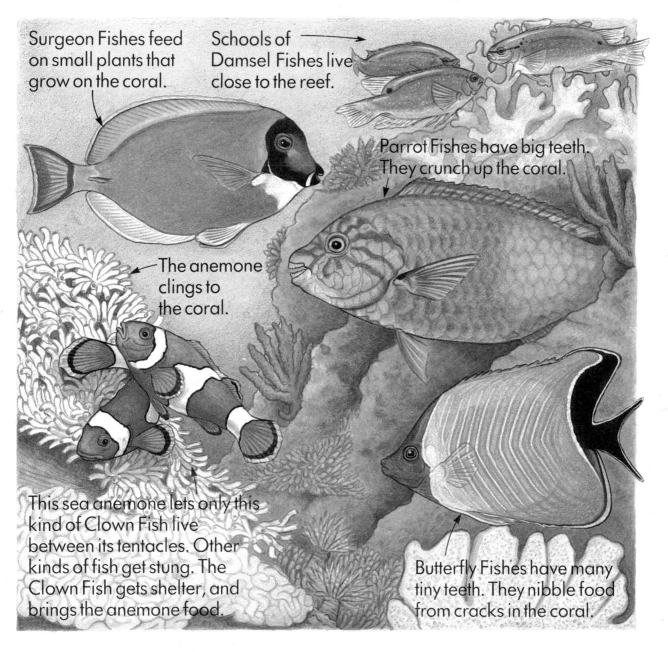

Surgeon Fishes feed on small plants that grow on the coral.

Schools of Damsel Fishes live close to the reef.

Parrot Fishes have big teeth. They crunch up the coral.

The anemone clings to the coral.

This sea anemone lets only this kind of Clown Fish live between its tentacles. Other kinds of fish get stung. The Clown Fish gets shelter, and brings the anemone food.

Butterfly Fishes have many tiny teeth. They nibble food from cracks in the coral.

Life in the deep seas

The deep sea is a bleak place to live. It is dark and very cold. No plants and not many animals live there. The fishes have to make sure they catch whatever food is around.

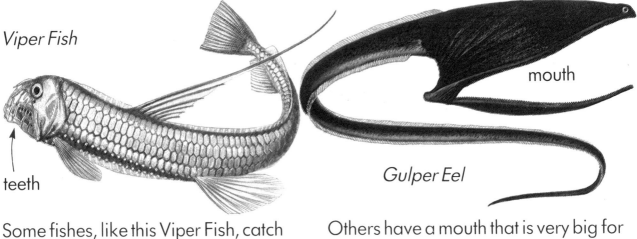

Viper Fish

teeth

mouth

Gulper Eel

Some fishes, like this Viper Fish, catch their prey with their big teeth.

Others have a mouth that is very big for the size of their body.

Many fishes eat small animals which live on the ocean floor.

Tripod Fish

long fins

Spiny-eel

Rat-tail

The Tripod Fish props itself up on its long fins. The long rays in these fins can sense food buried in the mud.

These two fishes swim with their heads down to find brittle-stars and small shrimps that hide in the sea bed.

Most deep sea fishes are black in colour. Some of them have special parts of their bodies that make light. When these lights are turned off, the fishes disappear into the darkness of the deep sea.

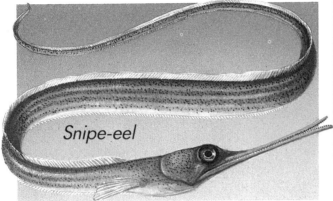

This fish has large eyes, so it can see quite well in the dark. It has no lights. It feeds on tiny shrimp-like animals.

Schools of Lantern Fishes keep together by flashing their lights on and off.

The Dragon Fish has a red light and a green light near each eye. It uses the lights like a torch to find food.

This deep sea Angler Fish has lights on its "fishing rods". It grabs other fishes that are attracted to the lights.

Picture puzzle

Each of the fishes drawn here has a tail from one of the other fishes. Can you work out which tail belongs to which body? Do you know the names of the fishes? The answers are at the bottom of the page.

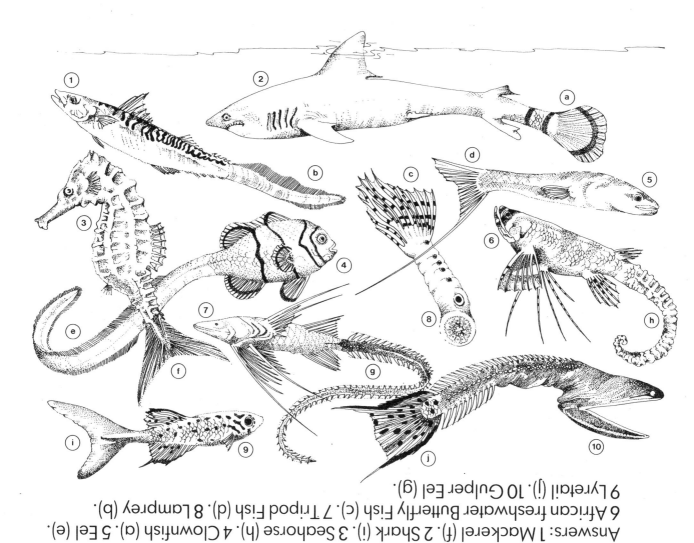

Answers: 1 Mackerel (f). 2 Shark (i). 3 Seahorse (i). 4 Clownfish (a). 5 Eel (e). 6 African freshwater Butterfly Fish (c). 7 Tripod Fish (d). 8 Lamprey (b). 9 Lyretail (j). 10 Gulper Eel (g).

TREES

Games

1. Hunt the Nut Weevil

Nut Weevils live on trees. Can you find 10 more Nut Weevils in the Tree pages?

2. Watch the leaf bud open

Hold the Tree pages like this.

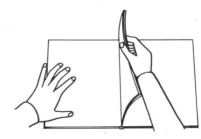

Watch the top right hand corner and flick the pages over fast.

watch here

Amazing facts about trees

Trees are the largest plants in the world. They also live the longest.

On a warm day in spring, a large tree like this takes up 250 gallons of water from the soil. The water would fill five baths.

Trees cover about one third of the earth's surface.

Sometimes, the roots of a tree spread wider than its branches.

Fossil leaf from a Maidenhair Tree

Maidenhair Tree

Maidenhair trees today look almost the same as ones that grew 200 million years ago.

Bristlecone Pine Tree

This tree has been alive for 4,900 years. It grows in America.

People say that this tree has enough wood to make all these bungalows. It is the biggest tree in the world. It is 83 metres tall and 24 metres round the trunk.

This Sierra Redwood tree grows in California, in North America.

195

Trees in the countryside

This picture shows you some of the places where trees grow. Some of them grow naturally and some are planted by people.

This is a windy hillside. The branches of the trees grow bent over because of the wind.

Trees in a wood grow close together. They have thin trunks and not very many lower branches.

People sometimes plant trees around their houses to protect them from wind and frost.

A tree growing on its own has spreading branches.

Some trees grow near water.

Few trees can grow here. It is too cold and windy.

Foresters plant pine and spruce trees in straight lines. These trees grow very quickly.

Trees are sometimes planted along roads to give shade.

Every few years, some of the trees are cut down. This gives the stronger trees more room to grow.

Trees often mark the edges of fields. They also stop the soil blowing away.

197

Under the ground

Oak Tree

Roots help a tree in many ways. They take up water and minerals from the soil. A tree needs these to grow. They hold the tree in place and they also hold the soil together. On steep ground, they help stop the soil from washing away in the rain.

These roots are very strong and woody. They help to hold the tree firmly in the ground and stop it from blowing over.

Worm

This grub eats soft, new roots.

The roots grow a little thicker each year.

Each tree has a main root. This is called the tap root. It grows deep and straight into the ground.

If a root comes to a stone, it grows around it.

Dead leaves fall to the ground. Worms pull them into the soil. The dead leaves contain minerals, which the roots will use again.

Some fungi grow on roots. They help the tree to feed.

Feeding roots grow from the side roots. They take in water and minerals through their tips. After a few years they die. New roots grow and find fresh soil.

Side roots grow near the surface of the soil, where there is air and water.

Cockchafer grub

Root tips grow all the time. They push through the soil. They are covered with hairs. These hairs take in water and minerals.

All roots grow towards water in the soil.

199

How a twig grows

This is how a Beech twig grows in one year.

This is the leading bud. It is covered with scales that protect it. The new stem and leaves are inside the scales.

These are side buds.

1. Winter

The side buds grow into side shoots.

The new stem grows and the leaves unfold. The scales are pushed apart.

The new leaves are soft and pale.

2. Spring

3. Summer

By summer, the stems are stiff and the leaves are dark green and shiny.

When the twig stops growing, it makes a new leading bud. Next spring, this bud will grow into a new shoot.

The leaves turn brown before they fall off.

Towards the end of summer, a new bud is made just above each leaf stalk. Next year, this bud will grow into a new side shoot.

This is where the leading bud was in the winter. The bud scales have left a scar. It is called a girdle scar. If you count the girdle scars on a twig, you can find out how old the twig is. This twig is two years old.

4. Autumn

Tree stumps

This is the inside of a healthy tree stump.

Most of the inside is sapwood. This carries water and minerals up from the roots to the leaves.

A very thin layer under the bark makes a new ring of sapwood every year.

In the middle is the heartwood. It is old, dead sapwood. It is very hard and strong.

Bark stops the tree from drying out and protects it from insects and disease. Bark cannot stretch. It splits or peels as the wood inside grows. New bark grows underneath.

This is how a tree may die.

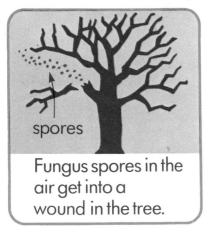

spores

Fungus spores in the air get into a wound in the tree.

The fungus spreads inside the trunk. The heartwood rots.

The heartwood in this tree is rotten.

Once the tree gets weak inside, it falls over in a storm.

When a tree dies, the bark becomes loose. Animals and plants can get under the bark. Many of them feed on the rotting wood.

Bracket Fungi grow on the trunk and feed on the rotting wood.

Slugs eat dead leaves and fungi. In dry weather they hide in cracks under the bark.

Longhorn Beetle

Bark Beetles and their grubs make long tunnels under the bark.

Scarlet Cup Fungi

Centipedes live under the bark. They come out at night to hunt for small insects.

Woodlice hide in damp places under the bark. They feed on rotting wood.

Millipedes live on the ground. They feed on dead leaves.

Deciduous tree leaves

Many trees are deciduous. This means that they lose their leaves in autumn. Most deciduous trees have soft, flat leaves.

Rowan

Lime trees lose their leaves in autumn.

The top side faces the sun.

Veins make the leaf stiff. Water and food travel through them.

The leaf stalk can bend so that the leaf does not break on windy days. Water and food travel through it.

There are hundreds of tiny holes on the underside. These open and close to let air in and out and water out.

Lime

Oak

Sycamore

Quaking Aspen

Horse Chestnut

Evergreen tree leaves

Other trees are called evergreens.
They keep their leaves all winter.
Most evergreens have tough, waxy leaves.

Pine trees have evergreen leaves.
Pine leaves are long and narrow.
They can stay alive in winter
because they are tough and
thick. Their waxy skin
stops them from drying
out. They can still make
some food in winter.

The veins
are in
lines.

*Monterey
Pine*

The leaves stay on evergreen
trees for several years. Then
they turn brown and fall off.
They do not fall off all at
once, so the tree always has
some leaves.

*Italian
Cypress*

*Snow
Gum*

Leaves are many different shapes, but they all do the same
work. Turn over the page to see what they do.

*Norway
Spruce*

Juniper

*Evergreen
Oak*

*Scots
Pine*

205

What leaves do

A tree breathes and feeds with its leaves.
Follow the numbers to see how a tree makes its food.

3. The leaves take in air.

4. The green colour in leaves makes food from air and water when the leaves are in the daylight.

2. The water travels up the trunk through tubes in the sapwood.

5. The food moves around the tree in special tubes. These tubes are just under the bark.

1. The roots take up water from the soil.

Why do deciduous trees lose their leaves in autumn?

Silver Maple

The corky layer forms here.

1. In autumn, it is not warm enough for leaves to make much food. Also, wind and cold weather would damage soft leaves.

2. A corky layer grows across the leaf stalk. Water cannot get to the leaf any more. The leaf changes colour.

This is the new leaf bud. Below it is the scar where the leaf was joined to the twig.

3. The leaf dries out and dies. The wind blows it off the tree.

4. All the leaves fall off. The tree rests until spring.

Tree flowers

All trees have flowers. Flowers have stamens, which hold pollen, and a pistil, which holds ovules. Pollen that lands on the top of the pistil grows down to join with the ovules. This is called fertilization. Fertilized ovules grow into seeds.

1. The petals and sweet scent attract insects. The insects feed on a sweet liquid inside the flower. This is called nectar.

Honeybee

These are stamens. They make pollen.

Cherry Tree

This is the top of the pistil. It is called the stigma. Pollen sticks to it.

2. When an insect comes to feed, it brushes against the stamens. Pollen rubs on to its body.

3. When it visits a flower on another tree, the pollen is brushed on to the stigma. The flower can now make seeds.

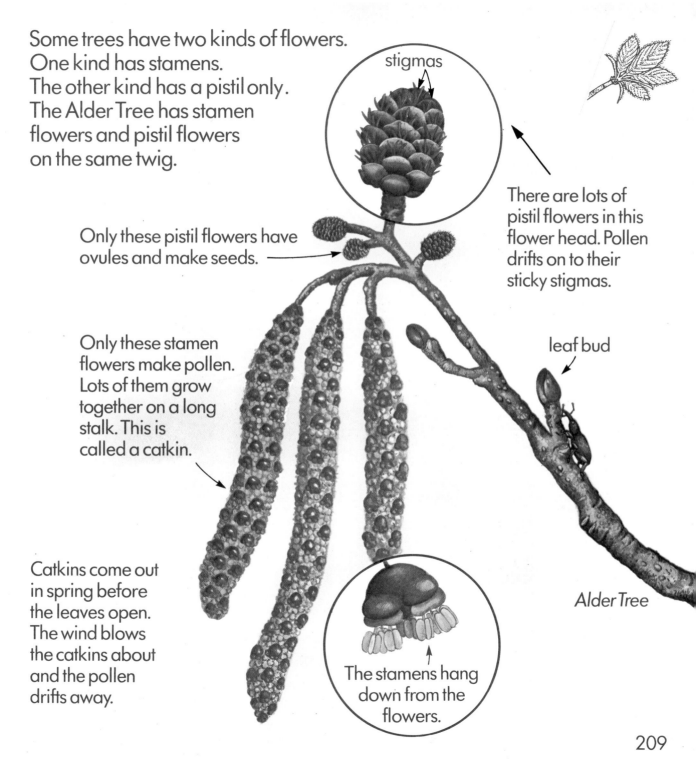

Some trees have two kinds of flowers.
One kind has stamens.
The other kind has a pistil only.
The Alder Tree has stamen
flowers and pistil flowers
on the same twig.

stigmas

There are lots of
pistil flowers in this
flower head. Pollen
drifts on to their
sticky stigmas.

Only these pistil flowers have
ovules and make seeds.

leaf bud

Only these stamen
flowers make pollen.
Lots of them grow
together on a long
stalk. This is
called a catkin.

Catkins come out
in spring before
the leaves open.
The wind blows
the catkins about
and the pollen
drifts away.

The stamens hang
down from the
flowers.

Alder Tree

209

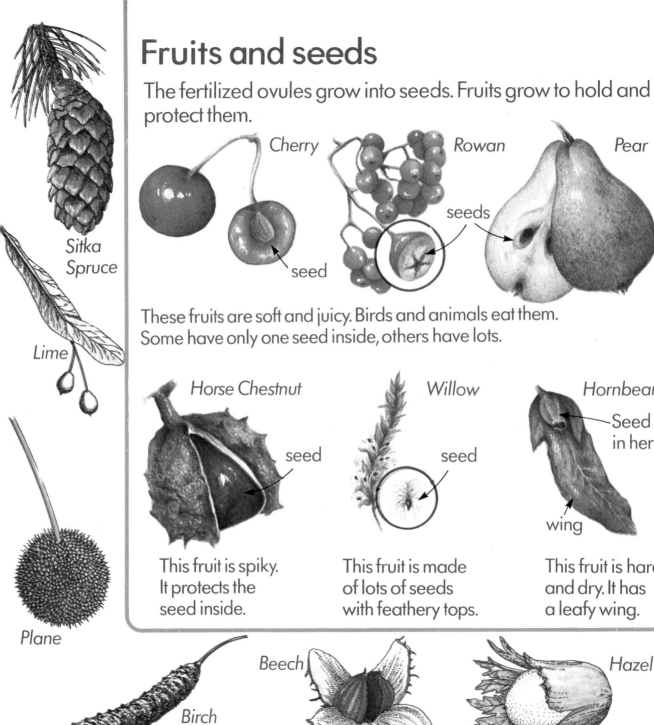

Fruits and seeds

The fertilized ovules grow into seeds. Fruits grow to hold and protect them.

Cherry

Rowan

Pear

seeds

seed

These fruits are soft and juicy. Birds and animals eat them. Some have only one seed inside, others have lots.

Horse Chestnut

Willow

Hornbeam

seed

seed

Seed is in here.

wing

This fruit is spiky. It protects the seed inside.

This fruit is made of lots of seeds with feathery tops.

This fruit is hard and dry. It has a leafy wing.

Sitka Spruce

Lime

Plane

Beech

Hazel

Birch

Many evergreen trees have fruits called cones. The flowers that grow at the tips of new shoots grow into cones. Sometimes this takes two years.

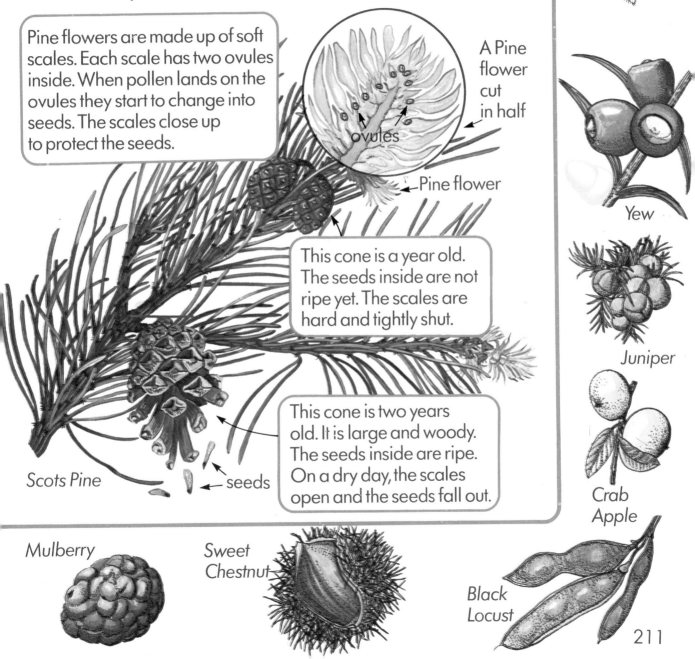

Pine flowers are made up of soft scales. Each scale has two ovules inside. When pollen lands on the ovules they start to change into seeds. The scales close up to protect the seeds.

ovules

A Pine flower cut in half

Pine flower

This cone is a year old. The seeds inside are not ripe yet. The scales are hard and tightly shut.

This cone is two years old. It is large and woody. The seeds inside are ripe. On a dry day, the scales open and the seeds fall out.

Scots Pine

seeds

Yew

Juniper

Crab Apple

Mulberry

Sweet Chestnut

Black Locust

How seeds are moved

When the seeds in the fruits are ripe, the wind or animals may move them away from the tree. There is not enough light under the parent tree for the seedlings to grow well.

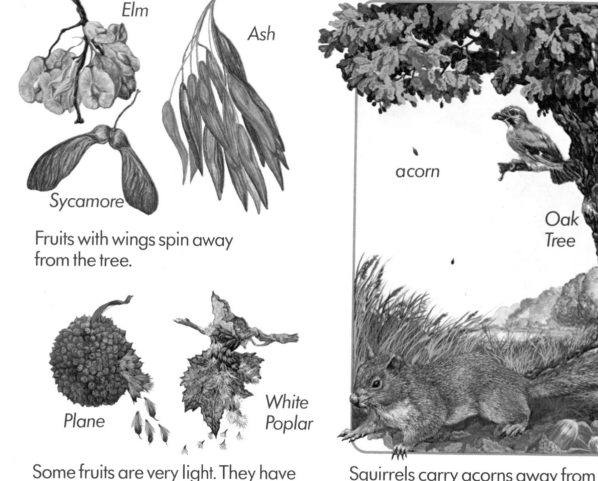

Elm

Ash

Sycamore

Fruits with wings spin away from the tree.

Plane

White Poplar

Some fruits are very light. They have tiny hairs that help them float away in the wind.

acorn

Oak Tree

Squirrels carry acorns away from Oak Trees and bury them. Birds feed on acorns and drop some. A few of the acorns grow into trees.

Birds carry the fruits and seeds away from these trees. They eat the fruits and drop the seeds.

Fieldfare

Holly

Blackthorn

Dogwood

Elder

Hawthorn

Waxwing

Alder cone

seeds

Alder Trees grow near water. Their seeds drop in the water and float away. Some seeds will be washed up on a damp river bank. They may grow into new trees.

Life on a tree

Keep a record book about a tree.
See how many insects live on the leaves or rest on the bark.
Watch how many birds visit it. Notice if any plants grow on it.

JUNE

I found a weevil on a leaf.

When I touched it, it folded its legs.

JUNE

I saw these willow fruits.

Herald Moth caterpillar

Some caterpillars are difficult to spot. Search carefully for them.

Dragonfly

Flying insects sometimes rest on the leaves in summer.

Willow fruits

Look for Willow fruits in spring and summer.

Poplar Hawk Moth

Some moths rest on the trunk in the day. They fly at night.

White Willow

Leaf Beetle

Look for beetles on the leaves and flowers.

Birds often visit trees to nest or sleep. Some search for seeds or insects.

Red Underwing Moth

These animals live on Willow trees. Willow trees often grow in wet places.

Picture puzzle

People eat many things that grow on trees. They make many things from the wood. There are at least 20 things in this picture that come from trees. How many can you find?

FLOWERS

Games

1. Hunt the Bumblebee

Bumblebees visit flowers.
Can you find 20 more
Bumblebees in
the Flower pages?

2. Watch the flower open

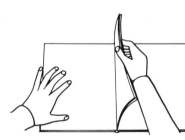

Hold the
Flower
pages
like this.

Watch the top right hand corner
and flick the pages over fast.

watch here

Looking at Buttercup flowers

If you look closely at a flower, you will see that it is made of lots of different parts.

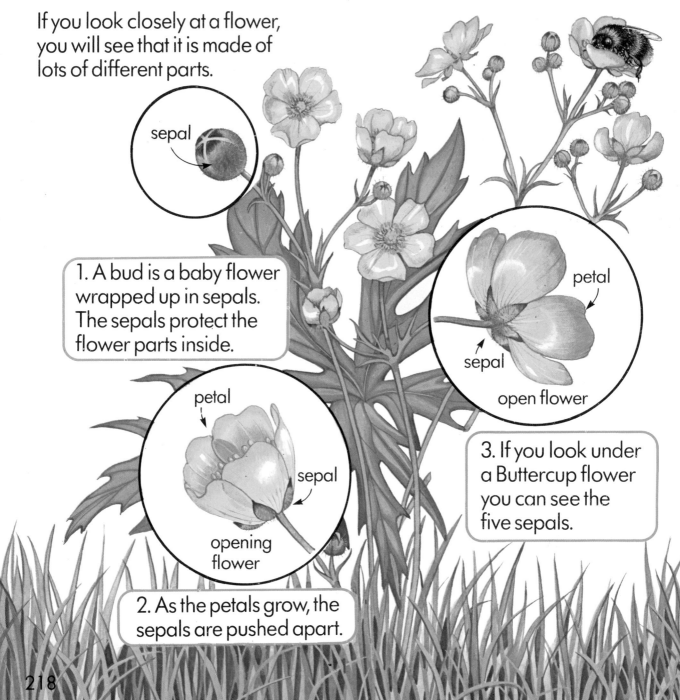

sepal

1. A bud is a baby flower wrapped up in sepals. The sepals protect the flower parts inside.

petal

sepal

open flower

petal

sepal

opening flower

3. If you look under a Buttercup flower you can see the five sepals.

2. As the petals grow, the sepals are pushed apart.

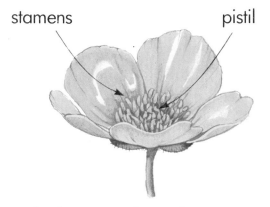

stamens · pistil

Inside the ring of petals are more flower parts. The green parts in the centre are called the pistil. Around it are stamens.

stamens · pistil

If you pull off the petals and sepals, you can see all the parts inside.

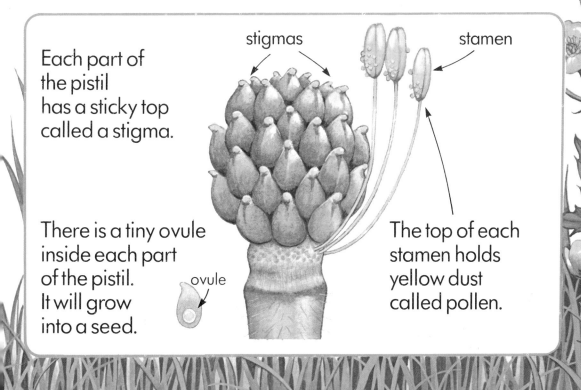

Each part of the pistil has a sticky top called a stigma.

stigmas · stamen

There is a tiny ovule inside each part of the pistil. It will grow into a seed.

ovule

The top of each stamen holds yellow dust called pollen.

Looking at flower parts

Flower parts can be different shapes and sizes and different colours. You will have to look closely at each flower to see which part is which.

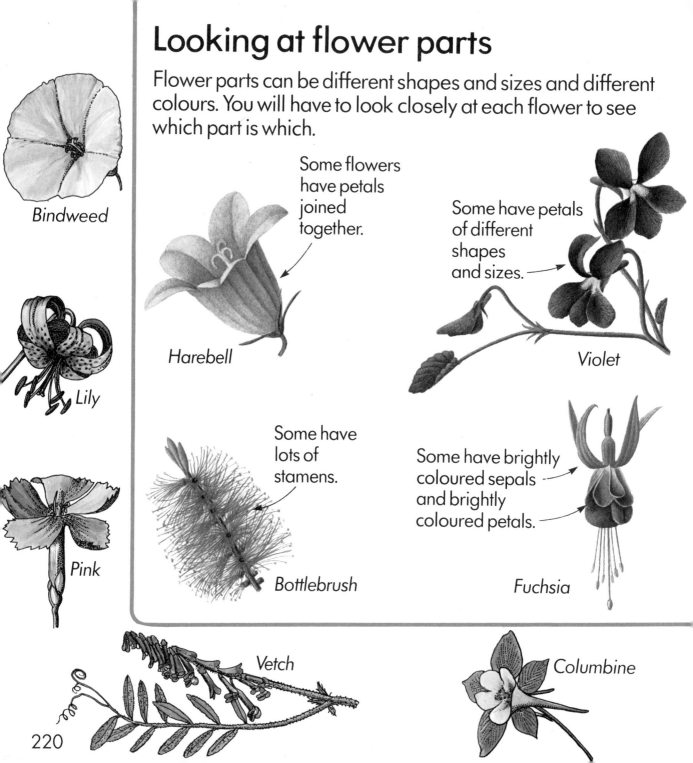

Bindweed

Some flowers have petals joined together.

Harebell

Some have petals of different shapes and sizes.

Violet

Lily

Some have lots of stamens.

Bottlebrush

Some have brightly coloured sepals and brightly coloured petals.

Fuchsia

Pink

Vetch

Columbine

Some flowers have a pistil with only one stigma.

Crocus

Daffodil

Some have a pistil with more than one stigma.

Cranesbill

An Aster flower is made of lots of tiny flowers.

An Aster has tiny flowers on the outside with one long petal.

If you pull an Aster to bits, you can see the tiny yellow flowers on the inside.

Daisy

The Bumblebee is somewhere on this page.
Do you know why he visits flowers?
The answer is on the next page.

Dandelion

Dahlia

The visitors

Cranesbill

Flowers have many visitors. They are usually insects, such as bees. The Bumblebee visits flowers to drink a sweet liquid called nectar. Sometimes the visitors eat some of the pollen.

Yellow Flag

Visitors to this flower need long tongues to reach down to the nectar.

Many flowers have guide-lines or dots that point the way to the nectar.

Nectar is in here.

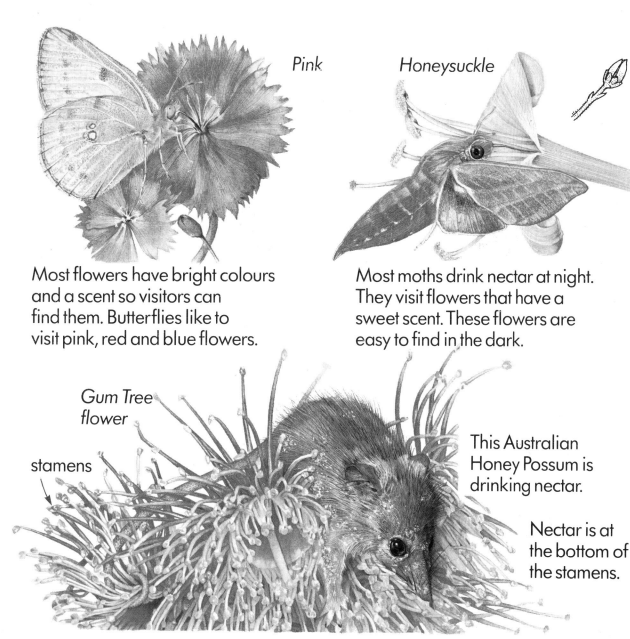

Pink

Honeysuckle

Most flowers have bright colours and a scent so visitors can find them. Butterflies like to visit pink, red and blue flowers.

Most moths drink nectar at night. They visit flowers that have a sweet scent. These flowers are easy to find in the dark.

Gum Tree flower

stamens

This Australian Honey Possum is drinking nectar.

Nectar is at the bottom of the stamens.

The flowers help the visitors by giving them food. The visitors also help the flowers. Do you know what the visitors do? The answer is on the next page.

Why flowers need visitors

Visitors help plants by moving pollen from flower to flower.

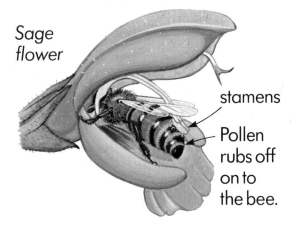

Sage flower

stamens

Pollen rubs off on to the bee.

pollen →

1. As a bee collects nectar from a flower, its body gets covered with pollen.

2. It flies to another Sage flower. It has pollen from the first flower on its back.

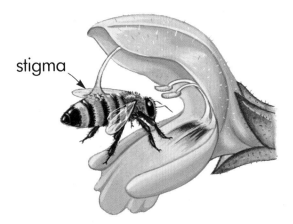

stigma

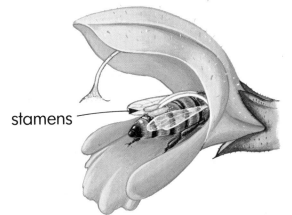

stamens

3. As it lands, the pollen on the bee's body rubs on to the stigma of the flower.

4. The bee goes into the flower. New pollen from the stamens rubs on to its back.

Fuchsia

Hummingbird

The Hummingbird is drinking nectar from a Fuchsia flower. It has some pollen from another Fuchsia flower on its breast feathers. As the bird drinks nectar, the pollen on its feathers rubs on to the stigma of this Fuchsia flower.

Watching for visitors

Find a flower that has stamens and a stigma that are easy to see. When the sun is out, sit down and wait for the insects to come.

Tulip

When the insect flies away, look to see if it has left any pollen on the stigma of your flower.

If an insect comes, try to see if it has any pollen on its body.

225

How the wind helps flowers

The flowers on this page do not need visitors to move their pollen. The wind blows their pollen from flower to flower.

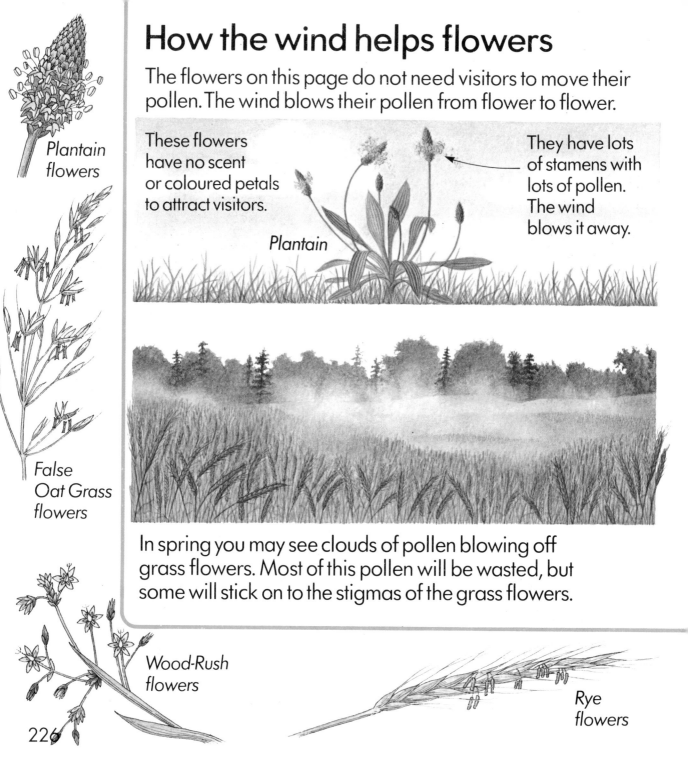

Plantain flowers

False Oat Grass flowers

These flowers have no scent or coloured petals to attract visitors.

Plantain

They have lots of stamens with lots of pollen. The wind blows it away.

In spring you may see clouds of pollen blowing off grass flowers. Most of this pollen will be wasted, but some will stick on to the stigmas of the grass flowers.

Wood-Rush flowers

Rye flowers

226

All trees have flowers. Many trees use the wind to move their pollen.

The Walnut Tree has two kinds of flowers. One kind of flower has a large pistil. The other kind of flower is made of lots of stamens.

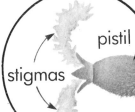

stigmas

pistil

stamens

pistil flower

3. If pollen from stamen flowers blows past a pistil flower, it will stick to the stigmas.

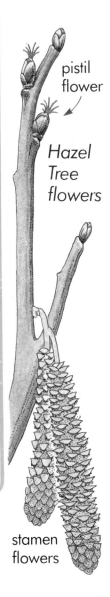

pistil flower

Hazel Tree flowers

stamen flowers

1. Lots of stamen flowers grow together on a stalk. Each stalk is called a catkin.

2. The wind blows the pollen off the catkin. Some of the pollen may land on a pistil flower.

pistil flowers

stamen flowers

Larch Tree flowers

227

What happens to the pollen

stigma

stamen

pistil

1. A bee has left pollen on this stigma. The pollen came from another Poppy flower.

2. Each grain of pollen grows a tube down inside the pistil.
There are ovules inside the pistil.

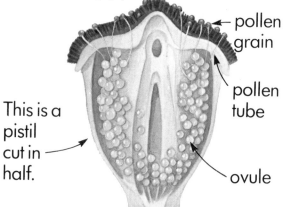

pollen grain

pollen tube

This is a pistil cut in half.

ovule

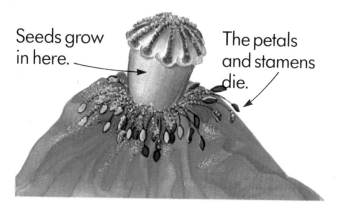

Seeds grow in here.

The petals and stamens die.

3. When a tube reaches an ovule, the inside of the pollen grain moves out of the tube and joins with the ovule.

4. The ovules in the pistil have been fertilized by the pollen.
The fertilized ovules will grow into Poppy seeds.

The flowers on the Poppy plant can be fertilized only when an insect brings pollen from another Poppy plant.

A Poppy flower cannot use its own pollen to fertilize its own ovules. The pollen will not grow tubes down into the pistil.

Poppy pollen will not grow tubes in the Buttercup pistil.

More about pollen

Many flowers are like the Poppy. They do not use their own pollen to fertilize themselves. Pollen must be brought from another flower of the same kind by visitors or by the wind.

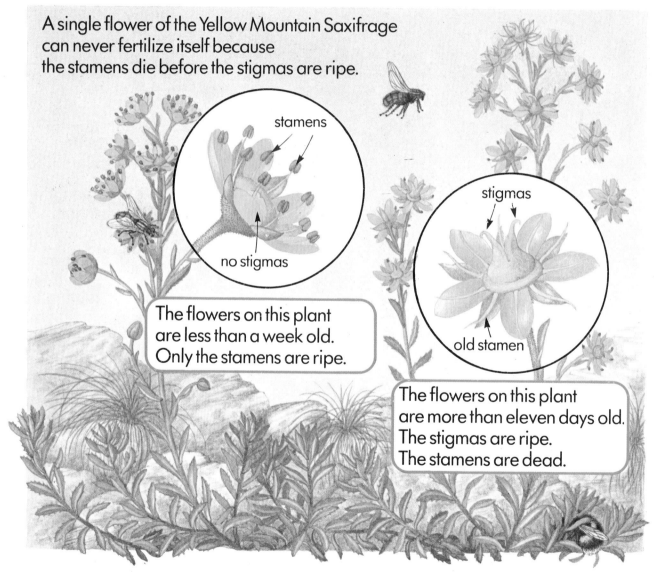

A single flower of the Yellow Mountain Saxifrage can never fertilize itself because the stamens die before the stigmas are ripe.

stamens

no stigmas

stigmas

old stamen

The flowers on this plant are less than a week old. Only the stamens are ripe.

The flowers on this plant are more than eleven days old. The stigmas are ripe. The stamens are dead.

The pollen of this Bee Orchid is moved only by male Eucera Bees. But if no Eucera Bees visit the Orchid it will use its own pollen to fertilize itself.

1. This Bee Orchid looks and smells like a female Eucera Bee. This is how the Orchid attracts male Eucera Bees.

Two sacs of pollen.

2. If a male Bee lands on a flower, the two pollen sacs stick on to his head.

3. This is another male Eucera Bee. He has pollen on his head from another Bee Orchid.

Stigma is in here.

4. As he lands on this flower, the pollen will stick on to the stigma and fertilize the flower.

If no Bees visit this Bee Orchid, it will fertilize itself.

This is how the Bee Orchid fertilizes itself.

The stamens bend over.

The Pollen sacs touch the stigma.

231

How seeds leave the plant

1. The ovules in this Poppy pistil have been fertilized. They are growing into seeds.

2. The pistil swells. It is now a fruit with seeds inside it.

3. Holes open in the top. When the wind blows the fruit, the seeds fall out.

Looking inside a seed

This is a bean seed. It has a thick skin to protect the parts inside.

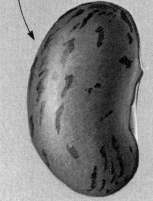

This tiny shoot will grow into a new plant.

If you split open a bean seed, this is what you will see inside.

This is a tiny root.

These are two seed leaves full of food. The shoot will use this food when it grows.

When the seeds in the fruits are ripe, the wind or animals may move them away from the plant.

Birds eat fruits and drop the seeds.

Because of their shape, Maple Tree fruits spin to the ground.

Sometimes animals bury fruits to eat later. The seeds that do not get eaten may grow.

The Cranesbill fruit springs open and its seeds fly out.

The wind blows away the Dandelion fruits.

Buttercup fruits may catch on to the fur of animals.

Plants make lots of seeds but only a few of the seeds will grow into new plants. The others die or get eaten.

233

How a seed grows

1. Autumn
A bird drops a Sunflower seed by accident.

2. Winter
The seed falls to the ground and gets covered over.

3. Spring
Rain makes the seed swell. A root grows down into the soil.

6. Late spring
The Sunflower plant grows a flower bud. The plant is now taller than a person.

← bud

7. Summer
The buds open.

Nasturtium

Pea

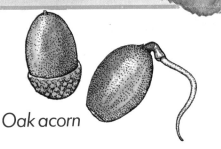

Oak acorn

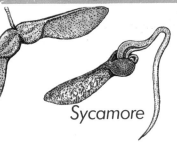

Sycamore

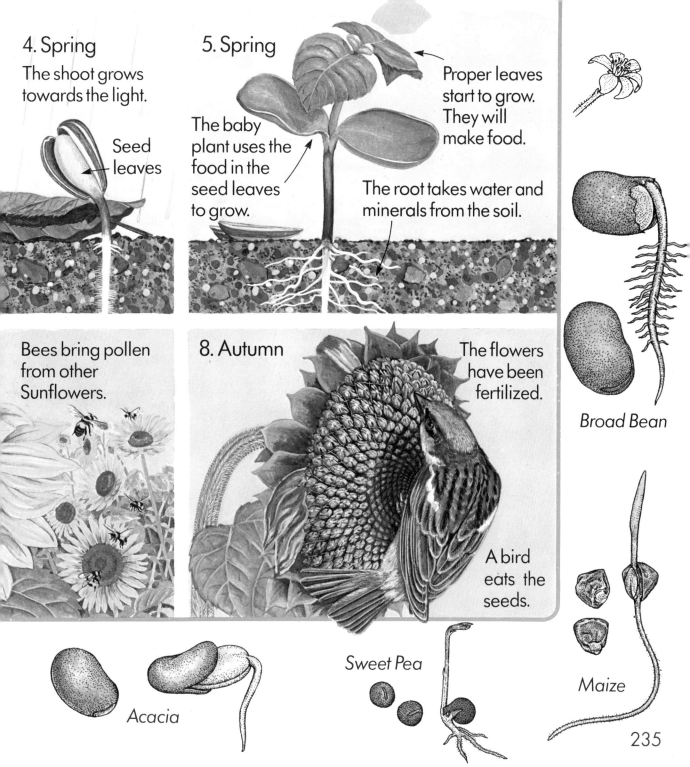

4. Spring

The shoot grows towards the light.

Seed leaves

5. Spring

The baby plant uses the food in the seed leaves to grow.

Proper leaves start to grow. They will make food.

The root takes water and minerals from the soil.

Bees bring pollen from other Sunflowers.

8. Autumn

The flowers have been fertilized.

A bird eats the seeds.

Broad Bean

Acacia

Sweet Pea

Maize

235

How flowers and insects work together

Flowers make most nectar and scent when their pistil or stamens are ripe because this is when they need to attract visitors.

Bees visit these Cherry flowers in the morning. This is when the flowers have most nectar.

New Honeysuckle flowers open in the evening. This is when moths visit them.

The flowers make lots of scent in the evening, but only a little scent in the day.

Bees visit these Apple flowers in the afternoon. This is when the flowers have most nectar.

Many plants take several weeks to open all their flowers. Bees come back to these plants day after day until all the flowers are over.

The Willowherb takes about a month to open all its flowers. The first flowers to open are at the bottom of the stem. The last flowers to open are at the top of the stem.

Willowherb or Fireweed

Horse Chestnut Tree flowers

New flowers open every day. They have lots of nectar. Yellow guide-lines point the way to the nectar.

new guide lines

old guide lines

When the nectar is finished, the guide-lines turn red. Bees do not visit old flowers with red guide-lines.

As each flower gets older, it makes more nectar. Bees always visit older Willowherb flowers first.

Keeping pollen safe

Most flowers try to keep their pollen safe and dry. Cold weather, rain and dew could damage the pollen or wash it away.

When flowers are closed, the pollen is kept safe.

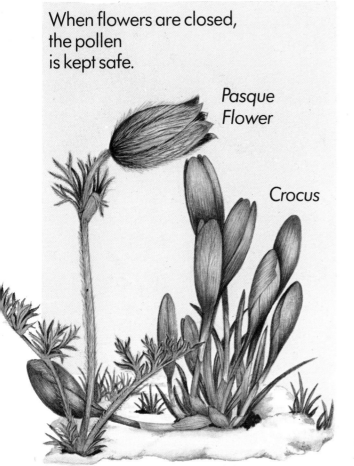

Pasque Flower

Crocus

When flowers are closed, rain and dew cannot get inside.

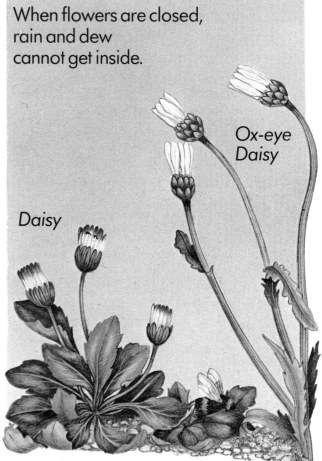

Ox-eye Daisy

Daisy

These flowers come out in early spring. The flowers open only when it is warm and sunny. If the sun goes in, they close up their petals. The flowers open again when the sun comes out.

These flowers close in the evening and in bad weather. If they have to stay closed for several days, they will fertilize themselves.

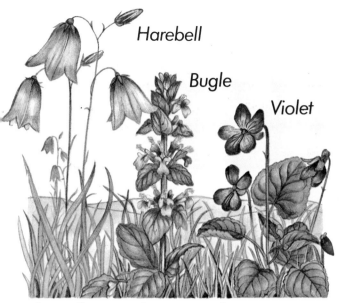

Harebell

Bugle

Violet

These flowers do not need to close their petals to keep pollen safe. Water cannot collect inside them.

Broom

Petals are closed

Petals open when a bee lands.

The stamens and the pistil of the Broom flower are kept safe inside the petals. They spring out when a bee lands on the bottom petals.

stamen has not split

pollen

stamen has split

Ripe stamens of Apple Tree flowers split open to let out the pollen. The stamens will split open only on warm days.

moth

New Catchfly flowers open in the evening. This is when moths visit them. But if the evenings are very cold, no new flowers will open.

Picture puzzle

There are nine flowers and nine fruits on this page. Can you guess which fruits belong to which flowers? You can see most of them in this part of the book.

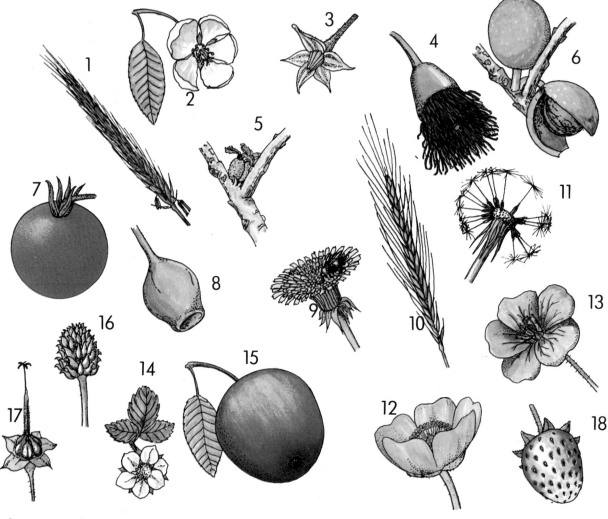

Answers: 1 and 10 Rye. 2 and 15 Apple. 3 and 7 Tomato. 4 and 8 Red Flowering Gum Tree. 5 and 6 Walnut. 9 and 11 Dandelion. 12 and 16 Buttercup. 13 and 17 Cranesbill. 14 and 18 Strawberry.

Index